Towards an integrated and sustaina

CW00384024

Abila Sylvanus

Towards an integrated and sustainable environmental policy frame work

LAP LAMBERT Academic Publishing

Imprint

Any brand names and product names mentioned in this book are subject to trademark, brand or patent protection and are trademarks or registered trademarks of their respective holders. The use of brand names, product names, common names, trade names, product descriptions etc. even without a particular marking in this work is in no way to be construed to mean that such names may be regarded as unrestricted in respect of trademark and brand protection legislation and could thus be used by anyone.

Cover image: www.ingimage.com

Publisher:
LAP LAMBERT Academic Publishing
is a trademark of
Dodo Books Indian Ocean Ltd., member of the OmniScriptum S.R.L Publishing group
str. A.Russo 15, of. 61, Chisinau-2068, Republic of Moldova Europe
Printed at: see last page
ISBN: 978-613-9-97298-2

Copyright © Abila Sylvanus
Copyright © 2018 Dodo Books Indian Ocean Ltd., member of the OmniScriptum S.R.L Publishing group

TOWARDS AN INTEGRATED AND SUSTAINABLE ENVIRONMENTAL POLICY FRAME WORK AND MANAGEMENT IN BAYELSA STATE OF NIGERIA

BY

ABILA, SYLVANUS, Ph.D

Contents

FORWARD

ON

WASTE MANAGEMENT AND SANITATION POLICY

The Ministry of Environment's every where in the world has a key vision to ensure the '*development* of a *sustainable, healthy, clean, pollution/toxic free* and *stable environment'.* Waste affects everyone, and there is a critical need for services to ensure that waste is managed in a meaningful manner, that contributes to the wider objectives of sustainable development and the mitigation of the detrimental impacts of climate change in Bayelsa State. Municipal solid waste from households and communities are a major source of pollution and emissions, which if managed improperly can result in harm to the environment and damage local communities. Ultimately, the ideal scenario would be to develop a zero waste policy and promote a green economy. However, this ideal is not achievable in the medium term and challenging at best in the long term. In the interim, a suitable policy on waste management is required to ensure the proper management of waste and to ensure sanitation in the State.

Regardless of the constraints of effective waste management, wastes should be viewed as a resource rather than a problem. It should be converted to a viable source of energy, as well as be processed to yield a sustainable source of secondary aggregates for ground improvement and land reclamation. Waste management should be utilised as a tool of youth and women empowerment and employment generation. This requires the development of suitable and sustainable waste management frameworks and policies, and the encouragement of waste management practices that help to achieve sustainable development and long term change. Government cannot act alone in the management of waste in the State, it has to engage positively with industries, civil societies, consumers and communities on waste management and it can foster the development of small businesses to engage in waste management.

CHAPTER 1

1.0 Introduction and Definition of relevant terms

Bayelsa State is in the Niger Delta of Nigeria, with an area of 21,100km^2 and has an estimated population of around 2 million, with Yenegoa as its capital. It is geographically located within Latitude 04° 15′ North, 05° 23′ South and longitude 05° 22′ West and 06° 45′ East. It shares boundaries with Delta State on the North, Rivers State on the East and the Atlantic Ocean on the West and South. The landscape is dominated by tropical rainforest, with thick forest to the north with arable land, and low lying mangrove swamps littered with a maze of meandering creeks to the south. A large part of this land is below sea level, with an estimated three quarters covered by water. The major occupations of the people in the State include fishing, farming, palm oil milling, lumbering, trading and crafting. Bayelsa State is a major oil and gas producing area and it contributes over 30% of Nigeria's oil production. There are hundreds of oil wells and flow stations across the state. Oloibiri in Ogbia Local Government Area of the state is where oil was first struck in Nigeria in commercial quantities in 1956. Gas production activities are currently being intensified in the State. The LNG Gas Supply Plant that supplies 53% of gas feedstock to the LNG plant in Bonny is located in Oluasiri in Nembe Local Government Area, and there is also a proposed network of associated gas gathering pipelines from the Nembe Creek oilfields to the LNG plant. The major oil exploration and production companies operating in the State are Shell, Agip and ChevronTexaco.

Responsible development of the natural environment is a priority for all countries and states, as globally agreed and outlined through a series of international conventions and summits. These advocate sustainable development and preservation of natural resources. Environmental sustainability and sustainable development is the Seventh Goal of the Millennium Development Goals (MDGs). 'Sustainable' means ensuring that activities for current needs do not compromise the needs of the future, while 'development' can be interpreted within this context to mean growth. The "environment" consists of all, or any, of the following media,

4

namely, the air, water and land; and the medium of air includes the air within buildings and the air within other natural or man-made structures above or below ground. "Pollution of the environment" means the release (into any environmental medium) from any process, of substances which are capable of causing harm to man or any other living organisms supported by the environment. This results in the contamination of the environment, with constituents which may cause or have potential to cause harm. "Contaminated land" is any (environment) in such a condition, by reason of substances in, on or under the land, that significant harm is being caused or there is a significant possibility of such harm being caused; or pollution of controlled waters is being, or is likely to be caused. The NESREA Act (2007) defined 'Environment' to include water, air, land and all plants and human beings or animals living therein and the interrelationships which exist among these or any of them. However, it is important to consider the integrated implications of what constitutes the environment, ensuring that the integration encompasses a context that includes the social and economic implications of what constitutes the environment, along with the interdependencies and relationship between these constituents.

The current state of the environment in Bayelsa State and most of the Niger Delta is left to imagination, with due cognisance to the legacy of pollution from oil and gas operations over the last few decades, exacerbated by sabotage and illegal artisan refining of stolen product and its associated pollution issues. Added to this are accidents associated with oil and gas operations, and January 2012 saw an explosion and fire on a Chevron rig in Southern Ijaw Local Government Area, resulting in a huge ecological disaster affecting over 40 communities. Also, low levels of sanitation and poor waste management practices particularly in urban areas has resulted in significant pollution of soils and water, presenting serious environmental and public health problem with both short and long term detrimental implications. This highlights the urgent need to ensure that legal requirements and instruments are clearly outlined and accessible, as well as coherent, integrated and transparent to ensure the effectiveness of the legislation and rule of law.

The activities of International Oil Companies as clearly being detrimental to the social and environmental benefits of communities, and often prioritise economic gains at the national level, which often neglect of the local areas, where extraction is being undertaken with all its associated negative environmental implications. A key goal of government policy is attaining sustainable development, and the activities in collaboration with operating companies and communities should therefore promote sustainable development. Oil industry and environmental related conflicts in the Niger Delta are thus perhaps a refection of the failure of previous administrations to implement effectively pertinent environmental policies, geared towards ensuring and sustaining sustainable development. A net consequence of this failure is also reflected in the frustrations of the local people and environmental movement groups about the processes which deter their agitation for improvement in local living conditions and development in the Niger delta. This should also ensure that appropriate levels of compliance are observed for developed environmental policies, thereby protecting public health, protecting livelihoods and preserving the natural environment.

Environmental responsibility and consideration must be put at the heart of decision making, ensuring that the broad objectives of sustainable development and climate change implications are appropriately encompassed, as well as the social implications of actions via community participation in the decision making processes. This explains the need for the generation of a robust and holistic Environmental Charter for Bayelsa State, one that is appropriately enforceable via the implementation of extant legislations at the State level to support and reinforce the National Transformation and Restoration agenda of the present administration as well as the buttressing and enhancement of institutional capacity to facilitate implementation. This policy seeks to present a working document on a holistic and integrated environmental policy framework, which will be subjected to iteration and consultation to provide a robust policy for managing, enhancing and regulating the environment in Bayelsa State, in addition to supporting socioeconomic growth as well as improving and sustaining appropriate levels of public health.

Collaboration and consultation with local communities are critical to ensure effective management of the natural environment and resources, and this can also serve as a pathway for employment generation and wealth creation in collaboration with other agencies, ministries. Some of the potential barriers perceived to effective development of appropriate environmental policies and management of the environment include:

- Lack of technical knowledge (institutional capacity)

- Limited baseline data (current state of the environment, sites, habitats, species)

- Limited resources for implementation and enforcement

- Poor community awareness on obligations and responsibilities

Definitions

The Bayelsa State waste management and sanitation policy has the primary aim of protecting the natural environment, preventing pollution and contamination of land, water and air, manage the disposal of hazardous wastes, promote sustainable development and protect public health. It will ensure sanitation in the State and sustain a healthy environment, under the provisions of the Environmental Sanitation Authority Law, 2006, and Refuse Collection and Disposal Law, 2006.

- The NESREA Act (2007) defined 'Environment' to include water, air, land and all plants and human beings or animals living therein and the interrelationships which exist among these or any of them.

- "Pollution of the environment" means the release (into any environmental medium) from any process, of substances which are capable of causing harm to man or any other living organisms supported by the environment.

- "Contaminated land" is any (environment) in such a condition, by reason of substances in, on or under the land, that significant harm is being caused or there is a significant possibility of such harm being caused; or pollution of controlled waters is being, or is likely to be caused.

- "Waste" includes any substance or object which the holder discards or intends or is required to discard, and any substance which constitutes a scrap material, an effluent or other unwanted surplus arising from the application of any process or any substance or article which requires to be disposed of which has been broken, worn out, contaminated or otherwise spoiled.

- "Sustainable Development" means ensuring that activities for current needs including growth and development do not compromise the needs of the future.

- "Hazardous waste" is waste that may cause particular harm to human health or the environment, and such wastes contain one or more hazardous properties.

Policy Introduction

Environmental Policy is written statement outlining commitment to managing the environmental impacts of its operations. The waste management and environmental sanitation policy must be concise, clear and transparent, with the primary objectives of promoting sustainable development, meeting the objectives of sustainable development, and mitigating the challenges of climate change. This will also outline the sustainable use of wastes as a resource, and implemented in conjunction with a waste management framework and the existing State laws of the Environmental Sanitation Authority, and the Refuse Collection and Disposal law of 2006. The framework will outline the strategy for waste management, ensuring that the policy provides clarity on waste management practices. Wastes should be viewed as a resource and the strategy for waste management will encompass:

- The provision of environmental objectives and management targets

- The outlining of provision to facilitate the development of infrastructure for waste management

- The specification of waste treatment and processing methods

- Communication of objectives and action plan to stakeholders

- Outline commitment to legal compliance and continuous improvement of the waste management and sanitation policy, as well as environmental pollution

- Promote resource efficiency during waste management, to tackle climate change, and take all opportunities to recover energy during waste management

Guidelines

This waste management and sanitation policy will encompass 5 core principles:

1. Principle 1 – The Waste Hierarchy: This outlines the hierarchy for waste management, which includes: waste prevention via minimisation; re-use; recycling; recovery (including energy and secondary materials); and then disposal.

2. Principle 2 – The provision of Waste Management Infrastructure: This outlines the infrastructure needs for effective waste management, including waste collection, processing, recycling and disposal.

3. Principle 3 – The adoption of a zero landfill policy, and a ban on public or open air waste burning, to ensure that all practices are sustainable and do not constitute and potential for environmental damage. This will promote the treatment of wastes in a way that can be utilised in land reclamation without contaminating the environment.

4. Principle 4 – The separation of management practices for hazardous waste, ensuring that the collection and management of hazardous waste are done along guidelines designed specifically for the specific hazardous waste streams.

5. Principle 5 – Sewage, wastewater and organic waste management: This outlines the requirements for managing sewage, wastewater and other organic wastes (food wastes and agricultural wastes), including the outlining of the specific infrastructure requirements for its management.

The requirements of the Waste Management and Sanitation Policy will include:
- Households and communities will be provided with waste bins along with

branded waste bin bags, to facilitate tidy storage of waste to be collected for disposal

- Providing a schedule for waste collection from households and communities, this will be scheduled for weekly collection from each household.

- Households will be levied in line with the Refuse Collection and Disposal Law, 2006, to facilitate the waste collection.

- Waste storage points will be strategically located around urban areas, where tricks will collect communal waste for transportation to processing facilities.

- Collected waste will be taken to a central waste processing and sorting facility, where recyclable materials will be separated and the waste materials processed.

- Incineration facilities will be developed within the State with integrated energy and material recovery from the waste incineration as outlined in the waste management framework document.

- The residue from waste incineration will be stabilised for safe use in land reclamation and other associated development.

- An appropriate recycling facility will be developed in the State in line with the Waste Management Framework, which outlines the priority materials for recycling. This will also include the development of zonal recycling facilities, where communities can take recyclable materials for disposal.

- Special requirements will be developed for specific hazardous wastes from industrial processes, to prevent the contamination of soil, water and air and the detrimental implications from these on human health.

The Bayelsa State waste management and sanitation policy will be enforced through the relevant State laws to promote:

- Adherence and potentially exceed of the Codes and ensure good practice.

- Compliance with statutory requirements – Environmental law

- Provide appropriate information, industries, training and supervisions to enable waste management, environmental protection and sanitation.

- Recycling all recyclable material when possible to enhance the environment.

- Mention a dynamic policy that complies with the enacted laws and revisions, codes of good practice and promotes the protection of the environment.

- Adopt a sustainable approach to the use of materials in waste management

- Improve the waste collection services to households and businesses

- Develop infrastructure to effectively manage waste in a way that is sustainable and contributes to the mitigation of the effects of climate change.

- Reduce carbon impacts from waste management, encourage appropriate waste management practices within communities, promoting re-use and recycling of materials.

- Support energy recovery during waste management

- Support measures to overcome the barriers in sewage, organic wastes and wastewater collection and treatment.

Reviews

The waste management policy will be reviewed annually and updated in line with the findings derived from the waste management framework developed for use with this document. This will be adopted in line with suitable legislation for enforcement in the State. The reviews will remove redundant content from the policy and incorporate new provisions as required.

CHAPTER 2

2.0 Integrated Policy Framework for Environmental Management in Bayelsa State

Environmental legislations are enactments and regulations embodying provisions concerned with environmental issues as they broadly affect land, water and air. Following the dumping of toxic hazardous wastes in Koko, old Bendel State in Nigeria in 1988, The Nigerian Federal Government moved to enact measures to ensure protection of the natural environment, including the enactment of the harmful waste Act 1988. This was enacted with the specific object of prohibiting the carrying, depositing and dumping of hazardous wastes on any land, territorial waters and matters relating thereto. This act was followed by the now repealed Federal Environmental Protection Agency (FEPA) Act and regulations (1991-2006), which was then integrated into the National Environmental Standards Regulation and Enforcement Agency (NESREA) Act in 2007. Other applicable laws and policies, as stated earlier include: The provisions of the Bayelsa State Environmental Sanitation Authority Law, 2006, Refuse Collection and Disposal Law, 2006, the Bayelsa State Public Health Law and the Bayelsa State Environmental Development and Economic Planning Law in addition to the Federal Acts, Sundry Regulations Policies on the Environment by the Federal Government including but not limited to the Constitution the Harmful Waste (Special Criminal Provisions) Act, 2004, of the Federal Republic of Nigeria, the now repealed Federal Environment Protection Agency Act, the National

12

Standards and Regulation Enforcement Agency, the Environmental Impact Assessment Act, 2004, the Oil in Navigable Waters Act, 2004, the Exclusive Economic Zone Act, 2004, the Land use Act, 1978 the Minerals Act, 1958, the Minerals and Mining Act, 2004 the Oils and Minerals Act, 2004, the Petroleum Act, 2004, the Relevant Provisions in the Criminal and Penal Codes the Proposed Petroleum Industry Bill (PIB), the Nigerian National Strategies and Goals on the Environment, the International Environmental Protection Conventions and Treaties applicable in Nigeria generally and Bayelsa State particularly.

Environmental policy is the formation of a planned action of environmental management and responsibility that will be followed by relevant institutions to achieve set out objectives or targets. This should foster and improve the quality of the environment, whilst balancing economic and social issues. It must have adequate scientific backing to succeed, and achieve an economic and social balance to be viable. Environmental policy is usually an instrument of authority to address environmental problems, and must be appropriately framed, partners delineated, and its implementation outlined and adhered to. Also, wide stakeholder buy in is required, from which a robust critique of the problem background is undertaken, and the relevant policy / policies are then appropriately formulated. This process should be interactive and iterative, and appropriate policy instruments developed to aid implementation of the drafted environmental policies. The selection instruments type will strongly depend on the prioritisation of partners of actors, and these instruments could be: regulatory – outline standards and compliance; economic – in the form of inceptives and subsidies; or informative – prioritising communication of the policy.

The Nigeria National Policy on the Environment (NPE) stipulates that "Nigeria is committed to a national policy that ensures sustainable development based on proper management of the environment in order to meet the needs of the present and future generations". Some of the goals of the NPE include: to secure for all Nigerians a quality of environment adequate for their health and well-being; conserve and use the environment and natural resources for the benefit of present and future generations; restore, maintain and enhance the ecosystems and ecological processes essential for the functioning of the biosphere to preserve biological diversity and the principle of optimum sustainable yield in the use of living natural resources and ecosystems, raise public awareness and promote understanding of essential linkages between environment and development and to encourage individual and community participation in environmental improvement efforts.

The NPE is holistic and comprehensive on environmental issues, highlighting action to strengthen legal, institutional, regulatory, research, monitoring, evaluation, public information and other relevant mechanisms for ensuring the achievement of sustainable development. Four areas in which results are expected from the strategies for enforcement of the NPE are: Establishment of adequate environmental standards; monitoring and evaluation of changes in the environment; publication and dissemination of relevant environmental data; and, prior environmental assessment of proposed activities which may affect the environment or use of a natural resource. The conceptual framework advocates achievement of the policy document through five major policy initiatives: preventive activities directed at the social, economic and political origins of the environmental problems; abatement, remedial and restorative activities directed at the specific problems identified (industrial production processes, problems from population pressures on land use, and problems from rapid urban growth); design and application of broad strategies for sustainable environmental protection and management at systemic or sub-systemic levels; enactment of necessary legal instruments designed to strengthen the activities and strategies recommended by the NPE; and establishment/emplacement of management organs, institutions and structures designed to achieve the policy objectives.

The Nigerian 1999 Constitution also make provisions for environmental management.

Section 20: "The State shall protect and improve the environment and safeguard the water, air and land, forest and wildlife of Nigeria"

Section 16 (2): The State shall direct its policy towards ensuring the promotion of a planned and balanced economic development.

Section 17 (2) (d) "In furtherance of the social order, exploitation of human or natural resources in any form whatsoever for reasons, other than the goal of the community shall be prevented".

These provisions within the 1999 constitution cannot however be enforced by legal action, since they are categorised under foundational objectives and directive principles of State policy and therefore non-justiciable. It is therefore curious that the issue of environmental protection appear not to be enjoying prominence in the Constitution of the Federal Republic of Nigeria, even though they are burning environmental issues in the country, with advocacy for its inclusion in the Federal statutory books. Currently, environmental compliance is regulated by NESREA as enabled by law, under the supervision of the Federal Ministry of Environment, while oil spill pollution control is regulated by NOSDRA. The Hydrocarbon Pollution Restoration Project (HYPREP) was also set up by the Nigerian Federal Government in August 2012 to facilitate environmental restoration and remediation of petroleum hydrocarbon pollution in Nigeria, as a consequence of a UNEP environment assessment of legacy pollution in Ogoni land. HYPREP is supervised by the Federal Ministry of Petroleum Resources, but has not yet been enabled by law via the Nigerian legislature, which clearly limits its functionality.

When it comes to integrated environmental management, there is no single compendium of environmental laws at the Federal level, rather there are various pieces of environmental laws, policies, guidance, which sometimes do not act or stand alone, but are rather embedded within other laws. Some of the relevant regulatory policies associated with environmental management in additional to the EIA Act (1992) include: National Policy on Flood and Erosion Control (2006), NOSDRA Act (2006) NESREA Act (2007), Land use Act (1978), Forestry Act (1958), National Inland Water Authority act (1997), as well as petroleum industry and energy laws in addition to relevant state legislations. The Environmental Impact Assessment Act 1992 is the core legislation that governs EIA in respect to projects in Nigeria, in line with the provision of principle 17 of the Rio declaration:

"Environmental Impact assessment as or national instrument shall be undertaken for proposed activities that are likely to have a significant adverse impact on the environment and are subject to a decision of a competent national authority".

One of the solutions to effective environmental management is the avoidance of excessively compartmentalisation (operating in silos), considering the synergies and overlap between and within the management of different aspects of the environment. A common template, similar to a planning policy framework for the environment will be ideal, promoting integration and ensuring common action for environmental management in collaboration with all relevant stakeholders. This can be phrased in the form of an integrated environmental policy framework – *'Bayelsa State Environmental Policy Framework'*, which sets out to provide policy for management of the different components required to ensure sustainable environmental management. The integrated environmental policy framework will set out to outline requirements for planning and managing the environment, enacting relevant laws to facilitate the environmental planning and management plan, to provide a framework for local communities and public health protection, developed in conjunction with existing legislation at the National and State level, with the associated formulation of new legal provisions to ensure success. This integrated environmental policy framework will encompass the three dimensions of sustainability to embed resilience with day to day operations, supporting the distinct roles from the economic, social and environmental components required to ensure sustainable development. Pursuing sustainable development involves seeking positive improvements in the quality of the built, natural and historic environment, as well as in community's quality of life.

This Environmental Policy Framework encompasses: Waste Management Framework; Flood Management, Erosion Control and Coastal Protection Framework; Biodiversity and Conservation Framework; and Pollution Control and Industrial Emissions Framework. These frameworks will be underpinned by appropriate policy instruments and associated guidance documents, buttressed by increased institutional capacity to manage, regulate and enforce the required schemes. To integrate these appropriately under an integrated policy framework, a series of environmental and social management frameworks are to be developed, which encompass the entirety of the State, not just specifically for the individual frameworks and activities contained therein, but also for the overlaps and synergies between the frameworks. Environmental and social management frameworks are used in cases of operations or activities with multiple sub-projects, where the entire range of environmental – social safe guard issues is not fully known. As a statement of policy, principles, institutional arrangements and procedures, project management for projects scoped for implementation will follow *inter alia* the following objectives:

- Ensure that sustainable development principles are adopted

- Integrate environmental and social considerations into project planning

- Ensure positive overall environmental and social impact, and manage any adverse impacts of projects

- Establish procedures, methods, guidelines, roles and responsibilities for programs or projects implemented

- Ensure compliance of regulatory and policy requirements

- Ascertain responsibilities and responsible agencies, while identifying modalities for estimating and budgeting implementation costs.

Outreach will prioritise social inclusion, engaging local communities in all aspects of operations, while ensuring that personnel requirements are addressed with appropriate training and capacity building. Funding options are to be explored, utilising local participation and funding where applicable, and establishing collaborations with international agencies e.g. World Bank, African Development Bank, e.t.c. to facilitate, in appropriate cases, the effective implementation of the Integrated Policy Framework for Environmental Management. The project strategy will also involve the development of appropriate terms of reference, where applicable which will then be followed by a work plan which includes: the review of existing information, a series of scoping activities to facilitate baseline data acquisition, delineation of specific projects including costing, implementation of these projects, and finally monitoring of effectiveness and impacts.

It is important to assess and understand the extent to which a policy has met its objectives, as well as to evaluate whether the benefits of the policy are being felt by those for which it has been designed. Environmental oriented laws are supposed to ensure **sustainable development**, check **gas flaring** and **oil spills**, as well as to **manage waste disposal**, particularly **hazardous wastes**. The efficacy and enforcement of the policy would also be prioritised, alongside increased environmental awareness and the integration of environmental concerns with all development. Also, it is critical to ensure legislative coherence, integration and transparency, as well as to strengthen the institutional capacity to ensure the implementation and enforcement of the policies. Each individual policy on an aspect of environmental management within the Integrated **Bayelsa State Environmental Policy Framework** would be concise, clear and easy to communicate, it would also have buy in from all relevant stakeholder. Also, all policies drawn up within the integrated Bayelsa State Environmental Policy Framework would be strategic in nature and adopt a risk-based approach.

CHAPTER 3

3.0 Biodiversity and Conservation

Natural resources have long been a source of livelihood for local communities in the Niger Delta, but pollution from gas flaring, oil spills (a key feature of the oil industry) and more recently artisan refining of stolen petroleum products, has destroyed farmlands, ecosystems and aquatic life. This therefore requires distinct policies for conservation of species and sites, as well as biodiversity protection, which would be linked and included in all new development planning within a transparent EIA process and procedure by which local communities can effectively engage in the process. This would consider the implications of climate change on ecosystems; facilitate fisheries and fish stock protection or conservation; ensure bio security and encompass robust policy principles with enforcement for species protection; facilitate protection of habitats and vulnerable sites; institute development controls; and ensure public health protection. Draft legislation would be developed to remedy pressing gaps in environmental governance, and ensure accountability in decision making. All threatened species and sites would be accorded favourable protection status, and where required, specific species or site management plans would be drawn up, which would embed site pollution control mechanisms. This will be in line with international best practice for managing vulnerable or threatened species, including those that are not yet critical with a few to future security of stocks.

Bayelsa State is blessed with an abundance of bio-diverse wetlands with interconnected creeks, marshland, mangrove swamps and rainforests. However, the legacy of petroleum operations (including sabotage) since its discovery in Oloibiri in 1956, in addition to indiscriminate logging, deforestation and other poor environmental practices has compromised the integrity of natural environment in the State. There is perhaps a call to delineate and designate large areas of wetland in the state as Ramsar sites (convention for the conservation of wetlands), to promote and protect the natural biodiversity of the State, aid in the recovery of vulnerable and endangered species, and mitigate effects of climate change. The Niger delta is one of the most important wetlands in the world (the entire Bayelsa is an important part of the delta or the centrepiece of the Niger Delta), it is the largest in Africa and third largest in the world. It is therefore important to conserve and preserve the integrity of this wetlands and its biodiversity. Apoi creek forest reserve is the only Ramsar site in the state and one of only 11 in Nigeria. It has an area of 29,213 ha (about 190km²) at 05°47'N 004°42'E, and is a tidal freshwater, lowland swamp-forest located in the Central Niger Delta, composed mainly of marshes, mangrove forests and fresh water swamps. The forest is dense and rich in several ecologically and economically valuable flora and fauna species. It is home to rare species, including the Niger Delta red colobus monkey (*Procolobus epieni*). Based on its restricted range and declining numbers due to hunting and habitat degradation, the Niger Delta Red Colobus is classified by International Union for the Conservation of Nature as 'Critically Endangered', currently listed as one of the world's 25 most endangered primates. It is hunted for bushmeat and threatened by logging and hydrological changes within the marsh forest. In the centre of its habitat is Apoi Creek Forest Reserve, a stronghold for the red colobus monkey. Today the area is managed by five surrounding communities: Apoi, Gbanraun, Kokologbene, Lobia and Okubie. The biodiversity value of Apoi Creek is universally recognized and in addition to the Niger

Delta Red Colobus, the marsh forest habitat is shared with two other threatened primates: the Nigerian white throated guenon (*Cercopithecus erythrogaster pococki*) and the red-capped mangabey (*Cercocebus torquatus*), each listed as Vulnerable in the Red List.

With increasing urbanisation and industrial development with excessive exploitation of natural resources, there has been a sustained, unmanaged and aggressive depletion of natural habitats and forest over the last few decades. The UN resolution on sustainable development highlights some of the social, economic and environmental benefits of forests and other natural habitats to people, and the contributions that sustainable forest management bring to meeting the objectives of sustainable development. The resolution also called for enhanced efforts to achieve the sustainable management of forests, including reforestation, restoration and afforestation, and to support all efforts that effectively slow, halt and reverse deforestation and forest degradation. It reaffirmed the intrinsic value of biodiversity, as well as the ecological, genetic, social, economic, scientific, educational, cultural, recreational and aesthetic values of biodiversity and its critical role in maintaining ecosystems that provide essential services, which are critical foundations for sustainable development and human well-being. It is also recognised that traditional knowledge, innovations and practices of indigenous peoples and local communities make an important contribution to the conservation and sustainable use of biodiversity, and their wider application can support social well-being and sustainable livelihoods. Without the support and contributions of local communities, no meaningful action can be adopted to ensure conservation and biodiversity protection.

To prevent any further deforestation, uncontrolled logging is being prohibited. In the year 2013 the Bayelsa State Government employed a total of 169 forest guards to police the forest reserves of the state. The present administration has also commenced an aggressive exercise of replanting indigenous trees and mangrove plants. Also, efforts are being intensified to re-engaged hunters into alternative sources of livelihood such as snail farming, fish farming or grass-cutter farming, or perhaps even into roles as rangers involved in the protection and monitoring of sites and species due to their knowledge of the local areas. Strict logging and hunting regulations / anti-poaching laws would be enacted and enforced, ensuring that local cultural factors as well as appropriate and adequate community engagement is embedded within all decision making and regulatory processes. Local community groups can be engaged in conservation, utilising appropriate environmental protection and management frameworks which are transparent, translated, easy to communicate and ensures access to information and the decision making process. This will create employment for the communities, particularly in the management, sustainable utilisation and the enforcement of bioresources to ensure biodiversity protection and the effective conservation and protection of the habitats and species.

Drafting a conservation and biodiversity policy either as a stand along policy or as one embedded within a similar or much broader environmental policy, would allow for the specific naming of a range of sites and site types, habitats as well as vulnerable species that need to be accorded special protection status. This policy should strive to ensure that the identification, documentation and vulnerability assessment of the sites, habitats and species that require special protection status, and clearly stipulate the engagement and enforcement action and responsibilities required to ensure their conservation and protection. This will encompass instruments for forestry and wetlands protection, must clearly stipulate the action for restoring the vulnerable systems and mitigating all current environmental degrading action, and detail the enforcement requirements and penalties for contravening the drafted policy. The institutional capacity to manage and enforce the regulations must be developed within the Ministry of Environment, through human resource optimisation and routine training. International best practice principles and sustainable development principles should take precedence in drafting the policy, which should mandate as a start, that information on species and sites should be collated to provide baseline information against which intervention can be compared to assess the efficiency of intervention action.

CHAPTER 4

4.0 Sustainable Development and Climate Change

The 1992 UN conference on Environment and Development, otherwise known as the "Earth Summit" of Rio de Janeiro generated an action plan for sustainable development in the 21st century, which has become the policy instrument that drives environmental programmes in most developed countries. This was further reaffirmed at the 2012 United Nations Conference on Sustainable Development (Rio+20), which also emphasises the needs for countries to strengthen institutional capacity and foster the development of green economies to ensure delivery of the overall objectives for sustainable development and poverty reduction. In agreement with the outcomes of the Rio+20 summit, Heads of Governments agreed to renew commitment to sustainable development, and to ensure the promotion of economically, socially and environmentally sustainable future for our planet and for present and future generations. They also agreed to further mainstream sustainable development at all levels, integrating economic, social and environmental aspects and recognising their inter-linkages, so as to achieve sustainable development in all its dimensions. Internationally agreed sustainable development goals which will encompass the millennium development goals will be agreed in 2015. In addition to the Rio conventions, member states were urged to fully implement their commitments under the United Nations Framework Convention on Climate Change (UNFCCC) and the Convention on Biological Diversity (CBD). Climate change is one of the greatest challenges of recent time and all countries and communities are vulnerable to the adverse impacts of climate change. These impacts are likely to increase left unabated, and we are already experiencing increased impacts including extreme weather events, sea-level rises, with coastal erosion and flooding, which is further threatening food security and efforts to eradicate poverty and achieve sustainable development.

The outline of sustainable development goals that will be developed by the UN for integration to policies after 2105 will build upon the millennium development goals. This will communicate the UN member states agreed and sanctioned post 2015 agenda for achieving sustainable development and poverty reduction. These goals will be action oriented, concise, easy to communicate, limited in number, aspirational and global in nature. It will also seek to promote the development of green economies within the context of sustainable development and poverty reduction, and will prioritise specific areas as agreed by international heads of governments required for the achievement of sustainable development. Scientific evidence indicates that human-induced global climate change is occurring and is having biophysical, social and economic impacts at local, state, national, regional and global scales. It is also likely to become more severe and unpredictable over the coming decades. Ensuring sustainable development requires the development and implementation of specific policies to support change adaptation and mitigation measures for undesirable consequences, to ensure that local communities are better equipped to manage the induced changes associated with the changing climate. It is impossible to separate climate change effects and requirements to embed sustainable development in every day practices, and whilst arguments can be made in some instances for the negligible gross 'local' contributions to emissions and regional industrialisation, the effects of climate change are likely to be pronounced in areas that are more vulnerable to small changes, such as large parts of low laying Bayelsa State. However, the legacy of petroleum exploration, exploitation, processing and distribution in Bayelsa state has in ways contributed to significant environmental damage, particularly from indiscriminate gas flaring from a climate change perspective.

The institutional framework for sustainable development should integrate the three dimensions of sustainable development (environment, social and economic) in a balanced manner and enhance implementation by among other things strengthening coherence, coordination, avoiding duplication of efforts and reviewing progress in implementing sustainable development. This should be facilitated via an action and result oriented approach that addresses cross cutting issues with the aim of fostering sustainable development. It is also important to understand the climate change impacts at a localised scale, including the spatial variation in impact, assessing both short and long term implications for local communities, particularly those in vulnerable areas prone to flooding and land degradation. A **climate change adaptation and impact mitigation plan for Bayelsa State** would also be developed, prioritising the establishing of **early warning systems, continuous data collection** for **predictive assessments** at the sub regional scale, and ensuring that communities have appropriate response plans for protection of lives, livelihood and property. Responding adequately will, in general, be costly, but it is, however, important to undertake detailed assessment of mitigation and adaptation costs on sector and location basis in order to plan effectively for responses. Detailed vulnerability assessment and analysis is needed for proper understanding of impacts, as well as to promote and foster socioeconomic development within the State and local communities. **There is a predicted 0.3m by 2020 and up to 1m rise by 2050 in average sea level for Nigeria. A large part of Bayelsa State is moderately lowland (stretch from Ekeremor to Nembe), most of it below sea level with a maze of meandering creeks.** This highlights some of the vulnerabilities faced by the State, particularly considering the socio-environmental implications of this, as well as the economic implications due to the concentration of vital oil and gas infrastructure in the area. This will also link in with a **biodiversity strategy** and action plan, to prevent the irrecoverable loss of vital species and habitats due to the induced environmental changes. However, it is important to avoid duplication of functions and any other potential conflicts that may arise from trying to develop policy which may clash with others already in existence. Bayelsa State already has a climate change policy in place, and it may be prudent to work within the existing framework currently in place or collaborate with said policy to draft a new framework more suited to meeting the challenges of a changing climate and increasing environmental and development uncertainty.

CHAPTER 5

5.0 Flooding, Erosion Control and Coastal Protection

Flooding, erosion and coastal vulnerabilities to sea level changes are rife in Bayelsa State, requiring a raft of ameliorative action to protect the citizenry and environment, including: Flood defences and protection, coastal protection, land degradation and soil erosion control (including slope protection), reforestation and management of wetlands, public health protection and socioeconomic development. Perhaps, this is the most critical of environmental damage in the State, second only to the pollution and associated health effects from oil and gas operations, which are more complicated to manage via State enacted and enforced policy or legislation. Looking at the different facets in isolation deters from a concerted effort to protect against damage induced by flowing water and or changes in water levels, the key requirement is to develop an integrated policy framework or plan that encompasses flood management, erosion control and restoration and the protection of shorelines.

Environmental and Social Management Plan – *flood management, erosion control and coastal protections*

Inherent within the natural terrain constraints of Bayelsa State are deeply embedded vulnerabilities to flooding and soil erosion, particularly for coastal communities along the network of rivers and creeks that dominate the spatial extents of the State. There is thus an urgent need to develop a robust and holistic ***environmental and social management framework for flood management, erosion control and coastal protection*** to ensure the protection of lives and property, as well as livelihoods of communities. All mitigation action will have to be implemented within existing EIA laws, ensuring that activities entailed within meet international best practice. The tasks detailed within this management framework will include:

- Screening

- Policy and regulatory framework

- Delineation of potential environmental and social impacts

- Development of management plan

- Strengthening of institutional framework

- Assessment of training needs and consultation

Potential positive impacts of clearly defined environmental and social management plan for flood management, erosion control and coastal protection will include:

- Reduced flooding – flood defences and flood plain management

- Reduced erosion and landslides

- Rehabilitation of degraded land (land restoration and reclamation)

- Increased vegetative cover

- Building resilience to climate change

- Reduced disaster risk

- Social impacts – employment generation, improved economic growth, agriculture, e.t.c.

Mitigation action considerations should be robust, holistic and engaging, ensuring that applications are thoroughly assessed for feasibility, local suitability, meet institutional requirements, encompass training requirements, include monitoring, and are cost effective in the long term. These considerations should be integrated into all mitigation action, and where required inform design changes for mitigation, preservation, rehabilitation, restoration, development and or diversification to ensure sufficient redundancies during protection. As part of assessments, the mechanisms to assess adverse impacts from any mitigation measure should also be assessed. The screening and scoping process should be used to identify priority areas for development, with the environmental and social management plan for flood management, erosion control and coastal protection underpinned by an adequate ESIA with emphasis on health, safety, environmental regulatory compliance, institutional responsibility and social inclusion.

Budgeting to outline interventions should include costs for:
- Framework development and verification

- EIA and Environmental Management Plan

- Monitoring and Documentation

Partners for developing suitable policy documents in collaboration with the State

Ministry of Environment (and associated departments or agencies) will include *inter alia*: State Ministry of Agriculture and Natural Resources, State Ministry of Water Resources, Bayelsa State GIS, Department of Erosion, Flood and Coastal Zone Management of the Federal Ministry of Environment; Nigerian Erosion and Watershed and Management Project (NEWMAP); Nigerian Hydrological Services Agency; Flood Early Warning System Centre of the Federal Ministry of Environment; NESREA and NIMET. To formalise the framework or management plan, a workshop or series of workshops will have to be facilitated which includes representatives of these partners, local communities, NGOs and the academic community. This will be followed by consultation on the outcomes of this workshop to inform the legislative and enforcement requirements of directives and policies for adoption. This will also require participation from the State Ministry of Lands and Surveys, as well as Bayelsa State Sustainable Development Strategy agency.

Factors such as the suitability of drainage channels and surcharge, particularly for heavy rainfall surcharge, will have to be extensively assessed, carefully documenting the soil erosivity and slopes erodibility indices for identified vulnerable sites within the State. This should be in the form of a State wide assessment, which also evaluates dredging and dredge practices, drainage channels and their integrity, and land use planning. This survey or State wide assessment will serve to:

- Indentify vulnerable areas

- Sensitise communities

- Explore areas to generate employment for communities through collaborations

- Collate baseline data

- Undertake initial scoping and project delineation for interventions

Collated baseline data should include a description of the status and trends of the influencing environmental factors or variables (all critical environmental and social parameters within each local community assessed), against which predictive changes and / or interventions can subsequently be compared. This should also include the installation of monitoring stations to detect environmental changes and obtain trends to facilitate predictions (collaboration with NIMET, Nigerian Hydrological Services Agency and Flood Early Warning System Centre of Federal Ministry of Environment). These assessments should include health impact assessments, and all proposed interventions should utilise local resources (materials and manpower) as much as possible to facilitate socioeconomic benefits for local communities. The goal of the Flood Protection, Erosion control and Coastal protection Policy will be to ensure coordinated and systematic measures for the management and control of the hazards and risks from coastal, soil and slope erosion and flooding, to reduce their impacts on the people and the environment. Nigeria currently has no clear policy directed at coastal zone management, and there has been persistent call for the country to have in place an integrated approach to coastal zone management.

Risk assessments should encompass both: Strategic flood risk assessments (sub-regional or State wide); and site specific flood risk assessments. This should also take into account climate change and change predictions whilst ensuring that flood resilience and resistance measures (residual risk management after events) are embedded within the policy. Strategies for implementation of the policy should be in line with the National Erosion and Flood Control policy, and include to:

- develop mechanism for forecasting, monitoring and control of erosion and floods

- review the land use laws and regulations

- promote and strengthen training at all levels in erosion and flood prevention, management and control

- creating public awareness to encourage participation

- protection of the marginal lands by limiting utilization to their carrying capacity

- subjecting resources users and developers to guidelines in order to reduce the vulnerability of the environment to flood and erosion-related disasters

- providing early warning systems to avert the escalation of flood and erosion hazards

Coastal communities have always historically adapted to changes in the water levels and coast line terrain, however, climate change is likely to exacerbate coastal flooding and erosion due to rising sea levels together with the potential increase in intensity, severity and frequency of coastal storms over the next few decades. These impacts have to be managed in a sustainable manner, requiring special considerations for development, mitigation and resource utilisation. Emphasis of the developed policy should be on resilience, ensuring that communities and resources utilisation are planned and managed in a manner that is disaster and risk adverse. This requires an understanding of the coastal changes over time, which should be communicated with communities to ensure that protective measures are put in place and managed locally by these communities, particularly when warning systems mandate the need for temporary evacuations to ensure protection of lives and property. This will require the development of very clear and distinct shoreline management plans for vulnerable coastal areas, which will be developed jointly with all relevant stakeholders and be subjected to regular iterative review to encompass all new adaptation measures. Management should hierarchal, adopting the principles of a risk management framework. This should encompass not just development or EIA mandatory type activities e.g. agriculture, dredging and the likes, but also spatial planning for communities and the development of strategies. This hierarchy should be in 5 steps:

Step 1 – Appraise all potential risks

Step 2 – Identify the priority risk areas

Step 3 – Avoid risk as best possible

Step 4 – Manage unavoidable risks

Step 5 – Mitigate all adverse impact

Flood management, erosion and coastal protection could be considered as one of the key priority environmental intervention areas for Bayelsa State, in addition to pollution control, for which the laws and intervention methodologies are still being developed or defined in terms of actions and responsibilities. A traffic light system should be developed for management of vulnerable areas for intervention:

Red   – Critical / Urgent actions required

Yellow   – Action or measured are required to prevent any further decline

Green   – No urgent action required

CHAPTER 6

6.0 Pollution Control, Permitting and Industrial Emissions

Environmental hazards from petroleum industry operations may be in the form of greenhouse gases, poisonous and carcinogenic chemicals produced as a result of product spills, gas flaring and other activities; or through the destruction of the fauna, flora, clean water, soil and the environment generally through oil spills and other oil drilling and handling activities. Bayelsa State has potentially one of the largest concentrations of onshore oil and gas operations in Africa, with a large number of annually documented spills and large volume of flared associated gas from exploration. Nigeria flares the second largest volume of gas in the world annually, accounting for 10% of all gas flared globally. The Nigerian Energy policy aimed to eliminate gas flaring in 2008, with the ultimatum moved to 2012 unsuccessfully. Also, a penalty system does not always work (policies impose fines for gas flared or spills incurred), and perhaps local utilisation options should be explored in collaboration with communities and the oil and gas operators at small scales to harness energy for utilisation. Also, avenues of collaboration as part of clean development mechanisms should also be fostered with the oil and gas companies operating in the State. Considering the national importance of the oil and gas industry, there is a limited degree of influence that can be exerted by State governments. However, there is sufficient scope to liaise locally with the operators within the State to ensure good environmental practices and environmental protection. With the pending Petroleum Industry Bill at the Nigerian legislature, as well as the Nigerian gas master plan, there will be scope to work together with the federal government and petroleum operators to improve the environment and better manage resources. The hope is that the Petroleum Industry Bill when enacted will present an opportunity for effective regulation of the petroleum industry, particularly for pollution control.

Petroleum pollution has become and integral part of the Nigerian oil and gas industry, resulting from a variety of factors including aging infrastructure, sabotage, poor maintenance practices, oil theft and bunkering. This environmental damage has stoked considerable ethnic tensions with significant security considerations. Environmental damage is a common occurrence, and oil spills have resulted in land, air and water pollution, severely affecting surrounding communities by contaminating water supplies, creating public health issues, destroying arable land and decreasing or severely affecting fish stocks. Whilst a vast majority of this contamination can be attributed to sabotage, oil theft and bunkering, and more recently to artisan refining (put-fire), poor maintenance and aging oil and gas operation and distribution infrastructure are often a significant reason behind spills.

A typical scenario of the scale and extent of contamination is observable from the concluded UNEP environmental assessment of Ogoni, which requires billion of dollars and 25-30 years of restorative action. With cognisance to the fact that large parts of Ogoniland are comparatively landlocked, Bayelsa State which has a myriad of creeks and swamps and other water dominated terrain. Also, the severity of the pollution in terms of scale, extent and legacy are much greater in Bayelsa State, added to the inherent terrain constraints which create severe inhibitors for the effective management of pollution.

Also, a framework for environmental health and perhaps occupational health should be developed, to protect communities as well as workers in industry from the adverse effects of unsafe practices and environmental damage. This can be embedded within a public health policy in collaboration with the State Ministry of Health, undertaking epidemiological assessments to evaluate the implications of legacy pollution on communities and ensure health protection. The Ministry of Environment in collaboration with the Ministry of Health is already undertaking a toxicological studies with other stakeholders from and outside Bayelsa State. Pollution control, permitting and industrial emissions policy should seek to harmonise environmental protection and pollution laws under a common policy framework, encompassing operations safety guidelines for industrial organisations, as well as inclusion of emissions standards for effluents and toxic waste leachate. Clear responsibility for spills and clean up should be clearly designated, including clear emphasis on local environmental protection, gas flaring and compensation for communities. Also, oil and gas pollution statutes and regulations should make it easier for victims of pollution to recover damages and compel clean up, utilising the polluters pay principle also emphasised duty of care and ultimate responsibility on the operating companies.

The Environmental Guidelines and Standards for the Petroleum Industry in Nigeria (EGASPIN) produced by the Department of Petroleum Resources (DPR) and revised in 2002, is in place for regulation of oil pollution from the petroleum industry. EGASPIN is designed to minimise oil pollution. It also sets out the approach to be adopted regarding contamination of the soil and groundwater, with the person responsible for the contamination required to restore the soil and groundwater to appropriate safety levels under threat of fines, potential imprisonment and loss of a license. However, being regulated by DPR, there are potential sources for conflicts of interest. Whilst the EGASPIN guidelines are one of the best in the world and perhaps perceived by some as being too stringent, the problem lies with implementation and enforcement, added to confusion as to whether EGASPIN represents a law or is merely a guideline that gains legitimacy from NPE or NESREA Act. It is these types of ambiguity that limits the effectiveness of regulation on oil and gas pollution control. At the national level, the clarification of target values and intervention values as well as the position and enforcement within a legal framework will have to be adopted, but this does not limit the ability of the State to effect measures aimed at protecting the lives and property of its citizens as part of environmental and health protection. Environmental and safety regulation is clearly a State function, but historically only in major events or what is classed as a 'tier 3' pollution incident takes place, will the State be the primary decision maker. Regulation and enforcement is the critical ingredient to avoid pollution and ensure pollution control with associated and appropriate restoration of all land degradation. Ensuring that suitable, concise and clear enforceable regulation for pollution control is available is critical to State exertion of pollution control regimes, added to the enacting of State legislation to plug all perceived gaps identified to ensure sustainable development and public health. The State must negotiate with all relevant partners to develop and implement pest practice guidance and environmental policy to manage pollution, particularly with the evolving oil and gas industry (increasing deep offshore and near shore operations) and the vulnerability of Bayelsa State to coastal damage (land, water and air, including livelihoods, habitats and species) and other petroleum pollution.

If deemed applicable, permitting regulations with emphasis on pollution control can be developed by the State, to regulate emissions of all non-oil and gas industrial operations, including dredging, land reclamation, mining spoils, and non-hazardous chemicals and industrial processing effluents and emissions. Hazardous wastes should be regulated under separate State policy, to work in compendium with

Federal regulations, buttressed by appropriate development of institutional capacity to disseminate, regulate and enforce all provisions as may be developed. Rather than rely on industry to adopt a 'goal setting' approach to managing emissions and effluents, the State should liaise with the environmental regulator NESREA, to develop more robust and holistic policy, which meets its unique and specific needs for development and sustainable environmental management. The critical issue with pollution control and emissions regulation will always be legislation and enforcement, one of the first steps required will be to assess all existing legislation to establish legal viability and enforcement options, before proceeding to establish means by which these can be buttressed to facilitate implementation and enforcement through State policy.

CHAPTER 7

7.0 Waste / Wastewater Management and Sanitation (Land Reclamation Utilisation)

Urban waste management is an integral part of city living, though holistic management of waste with integrated sustainable development principles tends to transcend urban systems, with a redirected emphasis on minimisation and conversation to more beneficial use. As such, waste management should be strategic, with a focus on medium to long term planning, using systems that advocate the core principles of sustainable waste management: reduce, reuse, recycle, convert to beneficial use, and finally dispose. Bayelsa State currently has a Sanitation Authority which manages the collection and disposal of municipal solid waste in the State capital. However, considering the environmental and public health vulnerabilities of the State and the delicate nature of the environment, there is an urgent need to implement suitable waste management that promotes the protection of the natural environment and human health. This should be in the form a policy statement for sustainable waste and wastewater management. This would include a long term service strategy for municipal waste management, which outlines waste collection and disposal plans and the responsible agency, including clear plans on how the collected waste will be processed for disposal. Waste management should be considered alongside other spatial planning concerns including predicted demographic and spatial shifts, with a planning focus that encompasses transport, housing, economic growth, natural resources management and regeneration, recognising the positive contribution that waste management can make to the development of sustainable communities, and should be integrated effectively with other strategies. Bayelsa State presents a unique scenario where significant amount of land reclamation is required for urban development, waste disposal should be undertaken in a way that allow the safe and economical utilisation of resources in ground improvement and land reclamation. Also, flood defences and other critical infrastructure can utilise processed waste as barrier systems and for the refilling of surface impoundments and burrow pits. Facilities should be put in place to enable waste collection and processing, as well as mechanisms for converting the waste to beneficial materials for reuse.

Wastewater management in Bayelsa State is likely to present more pronounced challenges, due to the present absence of piping of water and waste water systems, as well as an absent sewage collect systems for processing and ultimate disposal. This has led to result in the indiscriminate discharge of wastewater and sewage into the surround environments, which can cause pollution of the land and water with potential associated health effects from the release of pathogens and other health influencing contaminants. Aesthetics aside, this does not bode well for any civilised society, and considering the wealth creating implications of the petroleum industry in Bayelsa State, there is an urgent need to put in place clear and succinct policy to manage wastewater and sewage. Emphasis would be by education and awareness, followed by the development of small scale treatment facilities, to start cleaning some of these discharges, with priority being the treatment of faecal wastes from full or clogged soak away pits. This should be in the core developed communities in the State, followed by awareness and re-education programs in local communities on the health effects of poor sanitation and sewage management. With due cognisance to the needs for sustainable development, as well as the need for efficiency in waste management of all developmental action, the policy for wastewater management should as best possible encompass mechanisms for energy efficient treatment methods prior to disposal. Energy from waste mechanics should be prioritised where meaningful wastewater volumes are anticipated, especially for sewage and faecal matter from soak away pits. These can be treated via methods like **activated sludge treatment or anaerobic digestion** with associated generation of methane gas which can be reintegrated into the wastewater treatment process. Also, the policy should specify appropriate collection methods, which deter against the spillage of collected sewage or wastewater. This will also specify appropriate storage methods for the collected sewage, to ensure that aesthetics are not compromised during storage and that smell in not an issue for surrounding inhabitants.

Data on waste management should also be collated and documented regularly, and the waste management strategy should also be routinely updated to keep with evolving trends on generation and the management processes. There should be a concerted effort to ensure the optimisation of waste collection, with the development of suitable waste sorting and recycling facilities. The residual waste should be processed to beneficial use, particularly for land reclamation (*NOT LANDFILLING*), considering the urgent need for beneficial engineering aggregates for ground improvement in Bayelsa State. Where collated data on waste collection indicates that significant waste volumes are collected for sorting prior to disposal, there may be scope to consider the potential for energy generation during incineration of the municipal solid waste to create aggregate material for land reclamation. Conservative estimates indicate energy generation at 10MW from 100,000 tonnes of municipal solid waste annually. The energy generated can be dedicated solely for the waste treatment facility, and the waste management policy should ensure that sustainable development principles are embedded sufficiently within the strategy in the long term. The collated data should be used to make projections on waste volumes and treatment targets, and ensure that as the State grows with inherent demographic or spatial shifts, the strategy is sufficiently robust yet flexible to accommodate these changes.

The use of controlled and regulated incineration for waste management is perhaps the most efficient method for reducing waste volumes (waste reduction to less than 105 of the original volume), particularly for municipal solid waste. The residue from the incineration is an ash with suitable for use in land reclamation, due to its treatability to serve as a good engineering fill material. However, it is important to consider the presence of a variety of potential contaminants contained within this ash. The developed waste management framework / policy should ensure that prior to land reclamation with municipal solid incineration ash, the residue is stabilised with a cementitious binder, which will immobilise any contained contaminants, whilst also improving the quality and properties of the material as an engineering aggregate for use in fill for land reclamation. This will protect the natural environment and prevent any leaching of contaminants into water bodies. The policy document should clearly specify the assessment and evaluation methods for ensuring the treatment of this residue prior to land reclamation is suitable for the purpose for which it is intended. Where the State ministry of environment proceeds to develop its own laboratory, this will present the ideal platform for testing the viability and long term suitability of the stabilised secondary aggregates prior to use in land reclamation.

The benefits of developing a viable policy for waste and wastewater management in Bayelsa State are numerous, not less positioning it as a pace setter in developing effective environmental policies and setting the pace in aesthetically appealing environments. This will involve reorientation campaigns, aggressive waste reduction and recycling activities, waste disposal with industrial or development involvement, and sewage and organic waste processing. Some of the potential benefits will include:

- Promotion of business and public services including employment generation

- Infrastructure development and industrialisation

- Public health protection and wellbeing of the citizenry

- Environmental health protection and preservation of the natural environment

- Present a platform for sustainable development and community integration

Sub-Conclusions

Sustainable environmental management in Bayelsa State is a unique challenge that requires an integrated, robust, holistic and concerted effort, which will be implemented via a series of environmental policies which are integrated into the Bayelsa State Environmental Policy Framework. This will involve a series of catchment areas for the different policies within the integrated framework, targeting the vulnerable areas or priority areas for the different specific policies. These policies should be developed through an inclusive process, with the focus being on the overarching integration within a single or common implementation framework, with sufficient development of the institutional capacity of the Ministry to manage and regulate the implementation of the policy framework. This integrated policy will embed sustainable development into everyday environmental management, ensure that communities are sufficiently protected from the adverse effect of climate change, generate employment for local communities, foster public and environmental health protection, and reposition Bayelsa State as a pacesetter in Nigeria for sustainable environmental management and protection. The developed policy framework can be further buttressed by enacting relevant State legislation to facilitate enforcement, and the requirements of the different policy instruments can be iteratively communicated to operators and disseminated to communities to ensure that all relevant stakeholders are fully involved in the planning and decision making process. The integrated framework will encompass: a *Waste Management Framework; Flood Management, Erosion Control and Coastal Protection Framework; Biodiversity and Conservation Framework; and a Pollution Control and Industrial Emissions Framework*. These frameworks will be underpinned by appropriate policies with suitable policy instruments to meet the broad aims of the policies. This will ensure effective management of the environment, whilst embedding sustainable development goals to ensure the securing of the environment for future generations.

CHAPTER 8

Waste and Wastewater Management Framework: Sanitation and Environmental Protection Policy

8.0 Introduction

Effective waste management is essential in any urban society to ensure public health, environmental protection, and resource optimisation. Bayelsa State is a pacesetter in ensuring the protection of its citizens, and has recently been at the forefront of ensuring effective sanitation provisions for the State, mandating the development of suitable policies to ensure effective sanitation and safe disposal of waste in a manner that promotes and sustains sustainable development, poverty reduction and development of the State. Bayelsa State like most States in Nigeria is characterised by low levels of sanitation and poor waste management practices, particularly in urban centres, which has resulted in or has potential to induce significant pollution to soils and water, presenting serious environmental and public health problem with both short and long term detrimental implications. This highlights the urgent need to ensure that legal requirements and instruments for waste management are clearly outlined and accessible, as well as coherent, integrated and transparent to ensure the effectiveness of implementation of sanitation legislation and respect of rule of law. Measures are being taken to ensure appropriate waste collection and then adopt a sustainable management method that optimises beneficial reuse of waste in development. This will ensure effective waste minimisation, material and energy recovery and ultimately safe disposal, with the potential for utilising the disposal process for land reclamation. Besides the mandate for effective waste management, this will create opportunities to exploit material and energy recovery, as well as opportunities for small and medium scale businesses and cottage industries for waste processing. Bayelsa State is in the Niger Delta of Nigeria, with an area of 21,100km^2 and an estimated population of around 2 million, with Yenegoa as its capital. It is geographically located within Latitude 04° 15' North, 05° 23' South and longitude 05° 22' West and 06° 45' East. A large part of the land in Bayelsa State is below sea level, and a significant proportion of the State is covered by water. Inherent in the terrain constraints prevalent in the State, a large proportion of development require some form of land reclamation or ground improvement activity to make it fit for purpose. This creates an opportunity to engineer waste management to meet the industrialisation needs of the State, particularly for the safe reclamation of degraded land for sustainable development.

Responsible development of the natural environment is a priority for all Countries and States, as globally agreed and outlined through a series of international conventions and summits. These advocate sustainable development, preservation of natural resources and protection of the environment and public health. Environmental sustainability and sustainable development is the Seventh Goal of the Millennium Development Goals (MDGs). 'Sustainable' means ensuring that activities for current needs do not compromise the needs of the future, while 'development' can be interpreted within this context to mean growth. The "environment" consists of all, or any, of the following media, namely, the air, water and land; and the medium of air includes the air within buildings and the air within other natural or man-made structures above or below ground. "Pollution of the environment" means the release (into any environmental medium) from any process, of substances which are capable of causing harm to man or any other living organisms supported by the environment. This results in the contamination of the environment, with constituents which may cause or have potential to cause harm. "Contaminated land" is any (environment) in such a condition, by reason of substances in, on or under the land, that significant harm is being caused or there is a significant possibility of such harm being caused; or pollution of controlled waters is being, or is likely to be caused. The NESREA Act (2007) defined 'Environment' to include water, air, land and all plants and human beings or animals living therein and interrelationships which exist among these or any of them. However, it is important to consider the integrated implications of what constitutes the environment, ensuring that the integration encompasses a context that includes the social and economic implications of the environment, along with the interdependencies and relationship between these factors.

Figure 1 shows the waste hierarchy, which places emphasis on waste prevention, minimisation and reuse. This will be achieved through developing a suitable policy that promotes awareness campaigns and community education to promote waste reduction and reuse, before undertaking recycling and recovery then proceeding to undertake effective mass reduction, and then disposing (land reclamation) responsibly. In terms of recovery, the policy should be optimised towards some energy recovery from municipal solid waste, which will aim to recover as much energy as possible from residual waste after exhausting reduce – reuse – recycle option. *Efficient reduce – reuse – recycle – recovery mechanisms has potential to effectively reduce waste by over 90%*, with less than 10% of all generated waste requiring some form of ultimate disposal, in this case for land reclamation. The most effective waste reduction technology is incineration, which must controlled and environmentally acceptable with associated recovery of energy during the incineration process. Conservative estimates indicate energy generation of about 10MW from 100,000 tonnes of municipal solid waste processed annually. The energy generated can be dedicated solely to the treatment facility, and waste management policy ensures that sustainable development principles are embedded sufficiently within the long term strategy.

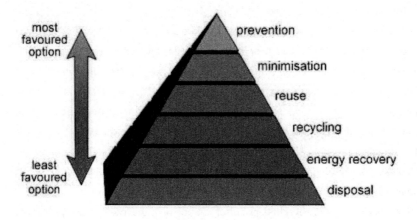

Figure 1: Waste Hierarchy

It is often easy to overlook wastewater management when developing waste management policy, particularly in areas where sewage is not piped to some form of central treatment facility. This has resulted in the indiscriminate disposal of sewage and wastewater to water courses, which often introduces faecal material with pathogens and other contaminants into the water with associated detrimental public and environmental health implications for citizens. The sanitation policy ensures that provisions are made for wastewater and sewage treatment for safe disposal, to ensure that discharges do not pose any health risks or environmental risks.

Waste and Wastewater Management Policy Framework

Environmental legislations are enactments and regulations embodying provisions concerned with environmental issues as they broadly affect land, water and air. Following the dumping of toxic hazardous wastes in Koko, old Bendel State in Nigeria in 1988, The Nigerian government moved to enact measures to ensure protection of the natural environment, including the enactment of the harmful waste Act 1988. This was enacted with the specific object of prohibiting the carrying, depositing and dumping of hazardous wastes on any land, territorial waters and matters relating thereto. This act was followed by the Federal Environmental Protection Agency (FEPA) Act and regulations (1991-2006), which was then integrated into the National Environmental Standards Regulation and Enforcement

Agency (NESREA) Act in 2007. There is also the harmful waste Act (1988) enacted with the specific object of prohibiting the carrying, depositing and dumping of hazardous wastes on any land, territorial waters and matters relating thereto. There is also the Nigerian Sanitation Policy (2004) which covers solid waste management, excreta and sewage management, food sanitation, sanitation inspection of premises, markets and abattoir management, adequate portable water supply, school sanitation, pest and vector control, management of urban drainages, control of animals, disposal of the dead, weeds and vegetation control and hygiene education and promotion. The targets set within the policy include the extension of sanitation to 80% of the total population by 2015, 90% by 2020 and 100% by 2025. However, it is clearly established and observed that a very small percentage of the population in Bayelsa have holistic sanitation facilities as outlines in the objective of the sanitation act.

Urban waste management is an integral part of city living, however, robust and holistic management of waste with integrated sustainable development principles tends to transcend urban systems, with a redirected emphasis on minimisation and conversion to more beneficial use. As such, waste management should be strategic, with a focus on medium to long-term planning, using systems that advocate the core principles of sustainable waste management: reduce, reuse, recycle, convert to beneficial use, and finally dispose. Bayelsa State currently has a sanitation agency which manages the collection and disposal of municipal solid waste in the State capital. However, considering the environmental and public health vulnerabilities of the State and the delicate nature of the environment, there are urgent plans to implement suitable waste management that promote the protection of the natural environment and human health. This takes the form a policy statement for sustainable waste and wastewater management. This includes a long term service strategy for municipal waste management, which outlines waste collection and disposal plans and the responsible agency, including clear plans on how the collected waste will be processed for disposal. Waste management should be considered alongside other spatial planning concerns including predicted demographic and spatial shifts, with a planning focus that encompasses transport, housing, economic growth, natural resources management and regeneration, recognising the positive contribution that waste management can make to the development of sustainable communities, and should be integrated effectively with other strategies. Bayelsa State presents a unique scenario where significant amount of land reclamation is required for urban development, and as such waste disposal is to be undertaken in a way that allow the safe and economical utilisation of resources in ground improvement and land reclamation. Also, flood defences and other critical infrastructure can utilise processed waste as barrier systems and for the refilling of surface impoundments and burrow pits. Facilities are tp be put in place to enable waste collection and processing, as well as mechanisms for converting the waste to beneficial materials for reuse.

Bayelsa State waste management should encompass appropriate science and engineering technology in ensuring that solid waste is collected and processed in a way that is suitable for the critical requirements of the State. This policy should mandate a strategic framework which is regularly updated, which will be developed by the Ministry in collaboration with relevant agencies and communities to ensure social inclusion. The *Holistic Waste Management Strategy* should encompass: *Business* and *Public Services*; *Infrastructure* and *Industrialisation*; *Health* and *Wellbeing*; and the *Protection* of the *Natural Environment* and *Resources*. State legislation should be enacted to:

- Create a strategic team within the Sanitation Agency to facilitate development of targets, methods and pathways for sustainable waste management

- Ban 'common' disposal of all hazardous wastes, which will be identified through a desk study by the policy development team. This team will identify and document specific toxic waste streams associated with industrial operations within the State

- Introduce levies for waste collection and establish a routine for waste collection

- Outlaw public waste burning and create waste dumping stations strategically around key locations in urban centres within the State

- Establish mobile courts for prosecuting environmental law offenders

- Perfect requirements for integrating community participation in waste

management

It is important to take into account issues of *cultural orientation* and *public awareness*, and there is potential for use of NGOs and community groups to *facilitate awareness campaigns and grassroots reorientation*. Waste collection will have to be structured in a manner that takes advantage of community preference and cultural traits typical to the communities being serviced. The sanitation agency should be buttressed by relevant modifications to its enabling legislation, to empower it appropriately to management and enforce the requirements detailed within the developed policy framework. This should make provisions for emplacing:

1. Waste Management Infrastructure – The strategy developed should outline very specific requirements for waste collection and processing. This will include the purchasing of *Waste collection wheelie bins (Figure 2) with supplied branded bin bags and Trucks for solid waste collection, development of waste dumping centres at strategic locations around cities (zonal centres), central facilities for sorting and recycling municipal waste, an incineration facility for waste incineration with energy recovery, and a treatment facility for the stabilisation of the municipal solid waste incineration ash for use as sustainable secondary engineering aggregates.*

Figure 2: Household Wheelie Bins with inserted bin bags, and large residential estate waste bins

2. Foster business and public service provisions for waste management. This should promote participation of private parties in waste management, fostering cottage industries participation in ground improvement and use of sustainable aggregates in land reclamation and the likes.

3. Facilitate the protection of human health and wellbeing and the protection of the natural environment. This should ensure that waste management is undertaken in a way that pollution is avoided and any existing contamination from previous waste management is remediated.

Wastewater management in Bayelsa State is likely to present more pronounced challenges, due to the lack central piping of water and waste water systems, as well as an absent sewage collect systems for processing and ultimate disposal. This has resulted in the indiscriminate discharge of wastewater and sewage into the surround environments, which can cause pollution of the land and water with potential associated health effects from the release of pathogens and other health influencing contaminants. Aesthetics aside, this does not bode well for any civilised society, and considering the status accorded via the wealth creating implications of the petroleum industry in Bayelsa State, there is an urgent need to put in place clear and succinct policy to manage wastewater and sewage. Emphasis should be education and awareness, followed by the development of small scale treatment facilities, to start cleaning some of these discharges, with priority being the treatment of faecal wastes from full or clogged soak away pits. This should be in the core developed communities in the State, followed by awareness and re-education programs in local communities on the health effects of poor sanitation and sewage management. With due cognisance to the needs for sustainable development, as well as the need for efficiency in waste management of all developmental action, the policy for wastewater management should as best possible encompass mechanisms for energy efficient treatment methods prior to disposal. Energy from waste mechanics should be prioritised where meaningful wastewater volumes are anticipated, especially for sewage and faecal matter from soak away pits. These can be treated via methods like activated sludge treatment or anaerobic digestion with associated generation of methane gas which can be reintegrated into the wastewater treatment process. Also, the policy specifies appropriate collection methods, which deter against the spillage of collected sewage or wastewater. This will also specify appropriate storage methods for the collected sewage, to ensure that aesthetics are not compromised during storage and that smell in not an issue for surrounding inhabitants.

CHAPTER 9

9.0 Implementation and Enforcement

To ensure the successful implementation and enforcement of waste and wastewater management policy, there is a need to develop a suitable strategic framework which outlines the specific processes to be undertaken during waste management. The first priority will be the evaluation of existing legislation, in terms of being fit for purpose, to allow synergy with the developed waste management policy. Legislation will be developed to address factors such as: levies for waste collection; time frames for waste household collection (ideally weekly); and requirements for management of industrial waste, waste oils and waste food from fast food chains. For aspects such as recycling and waste minimisation or reuse to be effective, benefits and incentives have to be communicated clearly in a language that the people understand and are willing to adhere to. Once the legislation and penalties have been communicated, and communities have been engaged to understand the needs and benefits of effective waste management, the strategy can be modified accordingly and communicated to the different levels. If people observe that household waste is collected weekly, that the roads and gutters are cleared regularly, and that stiff penalties exist for defaulting, they will naturally conform to requirements which will further increase efficiency and aesthetic quality.

There is scope for private participation under contractual agreements for operation of aspects of waste management processes, which can be particularly advantageous for waste collection, recycling, pre-treatment and segregation of wastes, provided effective standardisation and operation requirements are clearly outlined. This has cost saving benefits in terms of initial capital which can be tied into industrialisation strategies, and can links to cottage industries that will benefit from the waste strategy and associated energy and resources. Synergy, co-operation and collaborations on developing suitable strategies are a first step, using methods that are overarching, and which address the key requirements and meet the Ministry of Environment key vision to ensure the '*development* of a *sustainable*, *healthy*, *clean*, *pollution/toxic free* and *stable environment*'. Contractual agreements can also be utilised through inter-ministerial arrangements with the Ministry of Works, for initial utilisation of earthworks equipment during the early stages of developmental works.

The implementation of the waste management strategy as buttressed by the waste and wastewater management policy framework will include but not be limited to:

- *Optimisation of waste collection*: This will include outlining the requirements for the supply of bins (household and communal), trucks and manpower, including requirements for waste loading, transfer and segregation facilities. This will also incorporate the existing provisions in place for road sweeping; include collection of special wastes; green wastes from landscaping; market wastes; hospital and other hazardous wastes. Also, it outlines the requirements for the development of waste sorting and processing facilities, as well as the zonal waste dumping sites and recycling facilities. To optimise recycling, recycling centres will be strategically placed in urban areas in the State, including the development of 'tidy tips' where residents can go to dispose recyclable wastes. Figure 3 shows an example of a tidy tip site, where different recyclables can be disposed for reprocessing.

Figure 3: A typical tidy tip site for large scale recycling

- *Strategic Targets for Waste Management.* This will also outline the strategic targets for waste streams and treatment processes. Table 1 shows an initial target system for waste collection until 2025, while Table 2 shows the projections for solid waste management methods until 2025. Table 3 shows the targets for wastewater, sewage and organic waste management. Due to a lack of piped collection for sewage and wastewater, collection challenges are likely to persist in the medium to perhaps the long term.

Table 1: Bayelsa State Waste Collection targets – 2025

Percentage (%) Increase from 2014 Levels*	2015	2017	2020	2022	2025
Waste Collection Targets					
Solid waste (Household)	40	60	75	80	95
Solid waste (Industrial)	60	65	70	75	85
Solid waste (Communal Recycling)	20	35	45	60	75
Food waste (Including waste oils)	20	40	60	80	90
Special Waste	20	30	50	60	80
Sewage	10	20	40	50	60
* To be computed using current collection estimates					

Table 2: Targets for Solid Waste Management until 2025

Percentage (%) of methods adopted	2015	2020	20225
Solid Management Process Targets			
Incineration with Energy Recovery	73	70	60
Recycling	5	10	25
Recovery (metals)	2	5	10
Land Reclamation* (Burrow pit)	20	15	5
* Including residual incineration ash and incombustibles			

Table 3: Targets for wastewater, sewage and organic waste management

Percentage (%) of adopted methods	2015	2020	2025
Organic Waste Management Targets			
Composting	10	15	30
Anaerobic Digestion	40	45	60
Transfer to Solid Waste Management	50	40	10

- *Orientation and Awareness Campaign:* This will involve grassroots reorientation, including raising awareness and communicating the benefits of efficient waste management. This will also evaluate the modalities and requirements for effective community participation in the wider objectives of the framework.

- *Recycling:* The strategic framework will highlight the importance of emphasising waste reduction, reuse and recycling over disposal, and communicate the wider objectives of recycling and projected targets. It will also engage actively with relevant cottage industries that will benefit or partake in recycling and material recovery. This will also include the sourcing and provision of recycling bins and trucks, and the development of communal recycling centres (*Tidy Tips*). Optimal recycling streams will also be identified, including feasibility for collection (paper, plastic and metal).

- *Incineration with Energy Recovery:* This will involve using steam driven turbines to generate electricity during waste incineration, along with other mechanical and biological methods that can be used to create fuels for energy generation. Given the increasing priority to minimise waste for disposal, this is the most viable method of waste management currently available, and yields tremendous benefits in terms of *waste minimisation* (70% as a standalone) and *sustainable energy generation*. There is also scope for material recovery from the process. This will recover metals post incineration, and the residual ash is stabilised (cementitious treatment) for use in land reclamation, slope stabilisation, or as sustainable construction aggregate. A large initial capital is required for the implantation of the efw (energy from waste) incinerator plant, but the costs are recoverable in the medium term from waste management levies, energy and material recovery, alongside waste management.

- *Sewage and organic waste treatment*. This will involve putting in place facilities for organic waste treatment, using anaerobic digestion to generate energy and supplement incineration generation, and using composting to create manure for use in agriculture. Potential, facilities can be modified to allow for future expansion to treat waste water in the future, and the system can be integrated with the incineration plant to ensure sustainable use of resources (water for cooling and heating, gas for incineration, e.t.c).

- *Business and industrial opportunities*: There are a number of possible commercial opportunities arising from the waste management process, and these will be identified appropriately and documented as part of the strategy to ensure optimisation. Private sector participation will be actively encouraged, and an enabling environment should be created to support participation and growth.

Having outlined the strategic objectives, the infrastructural requirements will include: *Incineration Facility (efw through steam driven turbines); Anaerobic Digester (sewage treatment with energy generation) with onsite Composting; Recycling Centres (strategically positioned to optimise communal recycling), Waste Loading and Transfer Stations; and Waste Sorting and Segregation Facility*. Recycling will be undertaken through private sector participation, tailoring the cottage industries to the target streams and providing an enabling environment for the marketing or export of products. There are a number of other considerations that are to go into development of the strategic framework for waste management. Special Wastes such as Hospital Waste also require separate sorting and segregation to facilitate limited recycling. This will need to be rendered safe from infection and contaminants prior to any sorting, which can be done through High temperature (120°C) autoclaving to render the waste materials safe. The rest of the waste can be incinerated, and the heat recovered from the incineration process can be used to facilitate the autoclave process. Emphasis should be placed on systems integration, which will require extensive project planning to 'get it right first time', and have significant cost saving benefits. Also, there may be a requirement to supply different incineration streams during energy from waste processes, in case segregation is required with variable incineration requirements. These aspects will be facilitated in liaison with the incinerator designers, to incorporate as much as possible the requirements for an efficiently networked facility that is resilient to potential changes in future requirements.

Annual Environmental Summits will be used to disseminate the strategic objectives and incorporate stakeholder feedback, as well as to communicate the strategic objectives and commitments of the framework. These commitments should include but not be limited to the following processes:

- Establish clear outline of the waste management methodology, including targets to reduce the carbon impacts and associated climate change implications.

- Prioritise efforts to minimise waste generation, optimise reuse and recycling to encourage waste prevention, and support resource efficiency.

- Work closely with business sectors and materials industry to develop and sustain suitable cottage industries and thereby ensure improved materials and resources recycling.

- Actively support energy from waste (efw) approaches and initiatives to aid in achieving wider strategic objectives of industrialisation in Bayelsa State, including enhancing systems integration as part of holistic designing and project management.

- Work to overcome barriers from cultural orientation and complacent attitudes to waste management, particularly for sewage collection, recycling and payment of levies.

- Ensure that the framework provides sustainable approaches to use of materials (including during infrastructure construction), and delivers environmental and economic benefits.

- Provide initiatives that recognise and rewards participation in reduce, reuse and recycle for waste at the community level, which could be in the form of incentives.

- Set in motion a process for waste characterisation, and outline the indicators for successful implementation of the strategic waste framework, including the adaptation at the localised level to measure efficiency.

- Ensure clarification of regulatory requirements to reduce the burden on end users, ensure fair levy systems and actively prosecute offenders.

Waste Collection: Some waste collection mechanisms are already in place in the State, and it is important to identify what facilities are on ground and take advantage of these, to avoid duplication and to optimise resources. Required equipment for waste collection will include: collection trucks, which will vary depending on the required purpose (different trucks are required for collecting: household bin waste, communal skips waste, transferring waste, and for collecting recycling wastes); household waste bins, large street or communal waste bins, and waste collection bags (there is potential to manufactured this bespoke for use in the state, through the private sector participation, and can potentially be done using recycled plastics or other sustainable materials). Special waste bins and other provisions will also be made for specialised waste materials e.g. hospital waste bins, drums for waste oils at mechanic workshops and food eateries, and green waste skips at markets. Collected wastes will be taken to waste loading and transfer stations, or waste segregation and sorting stations. The exact requirements will vary with the different areas within the catchment, and the type and source of the collected wastes. Here, the waste materials will be processed as required, including dewatering and compression to optimise transportation volumes. Waste from street cleaning operations will require screening to remove sand prior to transfer, and the recovered sand can then be processed and used for construction, or as a backfill for land reclamation or to check erosion. Additional arrangements will be made for waste collection from large estates, corporate organisation or industries, and potentially include modalities for imposing a different levy scheme for this waste collection. Guidelines for corporate waste management, guidance on duty of care and environmental protection will also be communicated for managing industrial waste, and the existing mobile courts will be used to prosecute defaulters, with collected fines increasing the generated revenue.

Sewage collection will require the use of specialised collection trucks, given the absence of a networked sewage collection system. Enabling laws will be required to facilitate levied collections from full soak away pits, with the sewage used in combination with other organic wastes to create biogas and other resources for generating electricity. Cooking oil from eateries and fast food chains can also be used for the energy generation from biogas, or for the production of biofuels which can be tailored for use in special agricultural vehicles or other biogas fuel applications. Special arrangements and enabling laws will be used to facilitate routine collection, including the public health of consumers from excessive repeated use of the oil for frying. Waste food materials will also be collected specially from these facilities, including making special arrangements for collection from markets and farms. Waste oils from mechanics will also be collected and disposed of responsibly using anaerobic digestion with energy generation, but may require special or separate operations if residual sludge is used as agricultural manure, since the oil may contain contaminant heavy metals.

Recycling: Recycling involves the conversion of waste into a new product that is beneficial and or commercially viable. A large proportion of wastes generated by industrial and municipal processes are recyclable to yield beneficial products, but this is not economically viable given the cost implications of extensive waste segregation. The way forward involves encouraging source segregation as a habit and utilising community participation, after which the collected pre-segregated waste can be channelled appropriately for recycling by relevant industries. One of the biggest challenges for recycling in Bayelsa State like many others will come from *social and cultural orientation*, where people tend to accumulate material possessions, including junk that does not have any viable short or midterm usage. An effective awareness campaign will be used to sensitise residents on the need to support the recycling agenda, so that these waste materials can be converted to an alternative beneficial use. However, it is important to ensure that the recycling process does not become an opportunity for parties to feely disposal of hazardous wastes (including computer components, CRT monitors and some old electrical equipment). As such, it will be important to very clearly communicate the materials being recycled as part of the strategy, which should ideally include: *Paper, Plastics, Cardboard, Wood* and *Metals*. Recycling can also be optimised by utilising institutional / organisational participation, along with the street level provision of recycling bins. Private sector participation as part of a collaboration effort will significantly improve recycling in the State, as long as the need for recycling and benefits or incentives of participation is clearly communicated as part of the development of the framework. There is also scope and tremendous benefits of recycling special waste streams like car tires and scrap metal, with potential process applicability for export or domestic utilisation. Using shredded tire from old car tires processing as an example, the processed material can be used for a large number of applications. These include: light weight fill material; rubber mulch for gardens and children play areas; flooring material for play (e.g. basketball) courts and production of shoe soles; hot melt asphalt and recycled asphalt pavement for road pavement construction; infill material for grass-like synthetic turfs (astro turf – which can be used for building training pitches for the State stadium); for filling and packing materials among others. To optimise communal and large scale recycling, '*Tidy Tips*' can be deployed within urban areas in the State. The psychology around these tips encourages people to responsibly segregate large recyclable materials, which are collected centrally and then processed for delivery to recycling companies. These facilities must be strategically situated, to maximise efficiency and cater for the requirements of the catchment. They can also double as centres for collecting old clothes and books for charity, utilising NGOs and other charities in operation and management.

Organic Waste, Wastewater and Sewage: Organic wastes from households, organisations (food and livestock industry) and markets should be viewed as a viable resource, which if efficiently exploited will aid in the alleviation of energy deficiencies, along with the associated benefits of potential use for agricultural soil improvements from composting. These wastes can be used to supplement energy generation via EfW incineration, with generated methane gas combusted to drive steam turbines and generate heat and electricity. The anaerobic digestion processes break down organics to create CO^2 and Methane (variable content depending on waste type, but typically around 60% methane content), through methanogenesis processes via bacterial activity. Figure 4 shows a schematic for an organic waste treatment process. Sewage treatment is an essential requirement to ensure health protection and prevent the spread of diseases in communities. The collected sewage can be used to generate energy. The primary challenge comes from sewage collection, and operational staff health and safety. Small capacity tankers with pumps will be required for the evacuation of sewage from full soak away pits *at a charge*, which can then be transferred to sewage treatment facility for treatment.

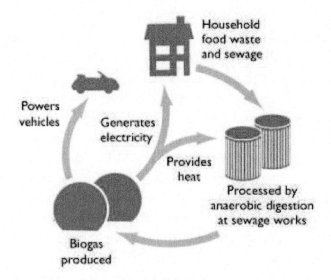

Figure 4: Organic waste treatment process

The requirements to ensure effective sanitisation have to be delineated and clearly communicated, to ensure safe working for staff, and odour control during collection and transportation. There is also the opportunity for waste water treatment at these facilities, as well as research on process optimisation and energy maximisation. For food and other organic wastes, there is a potential for the treatment of the anaerobic digestion residue and other composted organics to create bio-solids (biosods), which are very effective as manure for agricultural soils improvement. However, if waste oils and other organics from hazardous waste sources e.g. waste motor oils and other mechanic waste oils are used in the digester, then there is likelihood for inclusions of contaminant heavy metals in the sludge. Depending on the number of digesters in the treatment configuration, there may be a need to tailor the process for specific process e.g. purely for energy generation, with the waste residue dried for additional incineration. It will be important to ensure that adequate provisions are made for waste collection during initial designing of the framework, for market wastes, food waste (organisational and household), for sewage and for special organic wastes.

Incineration: Incineration methods for waste management have the potential to reduce solid waste by *70 – 90%*, requiring disposal of 10 – 30 % of total waste volumes. This is tremendously beneficial for waste reduction, but requires that sufficient measures are put in place to clean up the flue gases prior to release, to ensure health and environmental protection and climate change considerations. Also, the final residue (incineration ash) has to be disposed safely to ensure environmental protection, and incineration must be controlled to optimise the waste treatment process. Given the high temperatures attained during controlled incineration (over 1200°C), and the severe energy generation deficiencies in Nigeria, it is inconceivable not to consider energy recovery during the treatment process. Most countries including the UK have in place blanket ban on development of incineration facilities that do no incorporate '*energy from waste*' processes. The waste is processed for use as a 'renewable fuel' (help conserve waste oil and gas resources and increase energy generation) in specially designed power generation facilities (incineration plant with energy from waste), has *33% of the energy content of high grade coal*, and will *burn without any supplementary fuel*. It has the capacity to generate up to *600kWh of electricity per tonne of waste*, but this will vary depending on solid waste type. These incineration plants (energy from waste) use specially designed steam driven turbines to generate electricity, and have additional potential for heat recovery for use to supply nearby industries, use in the *sterilisation* (*autoclave*) of *hospital waste*, and use to *optimise anaerobic digestion processes*. These incineration plants have higher environmental standard that coal / oil fired power station, allow for ferrous metal recovery for recycling from the residue, which can also be used as a construction material with good engineering properties. UK operations records show energy generation of **5MW to 35MW, from 90,000 to 350,000 tonnes of solid waste annually** at facilities in Hampshire and Birmingham in UK. Figure 5 shows the dynamics of waste incineration with energy generation while figure 6 shows the schematics of energy generation from municipal solid waste incineration processes.

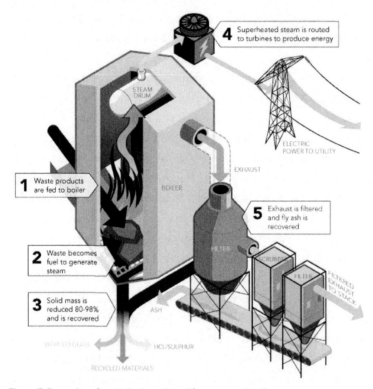

Figure 5: Dynamics of waste incineration with energy generation

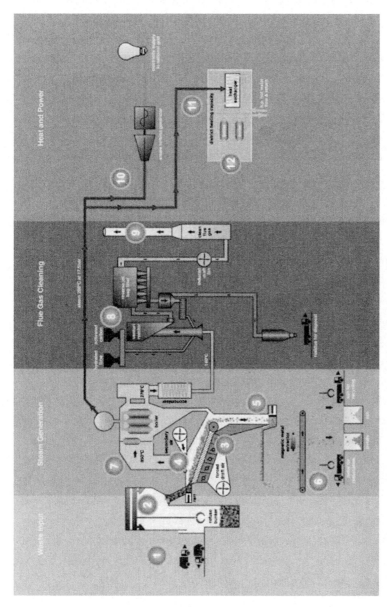

Figure 6: Schematic for Energy Generation from Municipal Solid Waste incineration

There are myths (based on perception) about incineration plants being major sources of pollution, being incompatible with large scale recycling, and being generators of large amounts of toxic ashes. These are largely baseless, considering the high standards employed, and the extensive flue gas cleaning processes in place at efficiently designed facilities. Also, metals and glass can be recovered after incineration from the ashes, with the generated ashes are often stabilised with hydraulic binders and used as construction aggregates and for land reclamation. However, measures have to be put in place to ensure safe working conditions for staff, and residents living around the facilities. Also, whilst it is easier to channel waste for incineration, effort should be made to actively encourage and promote recycling, which will be supplemented by materials recovery during waste sorting and segregation and post incineration. It is important to clearly characterise requirements during design, taking into account factors such as integration and interconnectedness demands, and the need for separate incineration channels within the facility for clinical waste. Also, while the generated energy should ideally be used to power localised industries, there is a need to consider additional redundancies to supply to the grid. This could be potentially beneficial where supply exceeds demand, or during down time e.g. at night where the industries are not operating. This will prevent wastage as electrical energy cannot be stored, and the facility should also be designed in excess of the current required capacity, taking advantage of potential for increased waste generation and potential to manage waste from other States. Appropriate measures for enforcement will be developed by the Ministry, which will also include the strengthening of institutional capacity and ability to manage the different components within the waste and wastewater management policy framework. The benefits will include: employment generation, waste management, environmental protection, health protection, strategic repositioning of the State for non-oil business development and industrialisation, land reclamation to name a few.

CHAPTER 10

10.0 Stabilisation for Land Reclamation

The use of controlled and regulated incineration for waste management is perhaps the most efficient method for reducing waste volumes (waste reduction to less than 10% of the original volume when combined with waste reduction and recycling), particularly for municipal solid waste. Incineration as the sole waste management method can reduce waste volumes by over 70%, but the remaining 30% may still need ultimate disposal. The residue from municipal waste incineration is an ash with suitable for use in land reclamation, due to its treatability to serve as a good engineering fill material. However, it is important to consider the presence of a variety of potential contaminants contained within this ash. The developed waste management framework / policy should ensure that prior to land reclamation with municipal solid incineration ash, the residue is stabilised with a cementitious binder, which will immobilise contained contaminants, whilst also improving the quality and properties of the material as an engineering aggregate for use in fill for land reclamation. This will protect the natural environment and prevent leaching of contaminants into water bodies. This policy document should clearly specify the assessment and evaluation methods for ensuring the treatment of this residue prior to land reclamation is suitable for the purpose for which it is intended. Where the State Ministry of Environment proceeds to develop its own laboratory, this will present the ideal platform for testing the viability and long term suitability of the stabilised secondary aggregates prior to use in land reclamation. Figure 7 shows the use of graded incineration ash for land reclamation as a backfill material.

Figure 7: Incineration ash being used as backfill material during land reclamation

However, there is a critical need to ensure that any contained contaminants, particularly trace quantities of heavy metals, do not constitute any environmental damage. This requires the stabilisation of the residue using hydraulic binders to immobilise any contamination for the long term. This chimes with current sustainability and resilience thinking, with the economical and sustainable utilisation of resources, and development of green technologies with principles of materials reuse embedded. However, no guidelines exist to ensure that these applications are well designed and properly implemented to ensure environmental sustainability. Suitable implementation frameworks have to be developed and validated as collaboration between the State Ministry of Environment and the Federal environmental regulators (NESREA). This will require chemical stabilisation using additives like slag cement or lime, which will then be processed into engineering aggregates which are relatively inert. The benefits of stabilised aggregate utilisation in land reclamation will be *invaluable* to *economic* and *industrial development*, with tremendous benefits for a wide range of sectors, including construction, urban development, environment and health. These benefits will include: *Employment generation* (direct jobs for people working in waste management, and indirect jobs for people involved in logistics), *Waste management, environmental protection and public health* (the primary aims are waste management and land reclamation, but the strategic objectives also chime with wider objectives for sustainable development, climate change adaptation and health protection*); Promotion of Investment and Industrialisation.* An outline of advantages will include:

- Resource Optimisation, by utilising waste products as sustainable aggregates for construction and land reclamation, while at the same time managing the disposal of municipal solid waste from existing waste dumps.

- Develop technological advancement by designing and validating methodologies for waste to construction aggregates technologies in Nigeria, including assessing the opportunities for beneficial commercial implications for the State.

- Generate green jobs for citizens, which chime with the current institutional mandate for sustainable development, as communicate at the recently complete UN summit on sustainable development in Rio, Rio+20.

- Efficient waste management, environmental protection and public health protection, by ensuring the conversion of harmful waste to a form that is beneficial for the public.

- Collaboration with other environmental initiatives to create pathways for strategic repositioning of the State, including the creation of industrial opportunities as part of the development of the State.

The primary objective of the policy from the perspective of land reclamation will be to e*stablish a feasibility assessment for the stabilisation treatment of* *the municipal solid waste incineration residue, establishing the leaching potential of contaminants to ensure long-term immobilisation*. The feasibility study will develop requirements through which incineration ash will be stabilised (methodology and optimisation being established though the feasibility study, which will be followed by a treatability and pilot study as part of the field implementation) to prevent the mobilisation of contaminants, when used for land reclamation. These *stabilised residues have excellent engineering properties for use as aggregates*, and will yield sites with excellent bearing capacities and engineering properties for subsequent development. *Cement stabilisation is an effective method for the containment of heavy metals*, which are typical components of incineration ash. The stabilised mixture will prevent the mobilisation of the heavy metals into the aqueous fraction, and thereby prevent any environmental pollution. This is chemical containment process, due to the modification of components speciation and encapsulation of contaminants, and these will be detailed as part of the development of technical guidelines and background for implement of the projects. However, there may be implication of using high grade cement (even though only small quantities are required) for stabilisation of incineration residue, which presents scope for developing a *small scale cottage industry to provide low grade or composite cements* that are suitable for the treatment process. This can encompass the use of limestone slag cements, using slag from iron processing or the use of composite limestone Portland cements. Research and treatment methods will adopt leaching assessment frameworks to design leaching tests and undertake predictive modelling for the waste treatment method. Also, independent consultants should be employed for verification of the treated residue, and the reclamation process should be verified through an inter-ministerial team from the Ministry of Environment, Ministry of Works and the Ministry of Water Resources.

General Conclusions

Data on waste management should also be collated and documented regularly, and the waste management strategy should also be routinely updated to keep with evolving trends on generation and the management processes. There should be a concerted effort to ensure the optimisation of waste collection, with the development of suitable waste sorting and recycling facilities. The residual waste will be processed to beneficial use, particularly for land reclamation (NOT LANDFILLING), considering the urgent need for beneficial engineering aggregates for ground improvement in Bayelsa State. Where collated data on waste collection indicates that significant waste volumes are collected for sorting prior to disposal, there may be scope to consider the potential for energy generation during incineration of the municipal solid waste to create aggregate material for land reclamation. The collated data should be used to make projections on waste volumes and treatment targets, and ensure that as the State grows with inherent demographic or spatial shifts, the strategy is sufficiently robust yet flexible to accommodate these changes.

The benefits of developing a viable policy for waste and wastewater management in Bayelsa State are numerous, not less positioning it as a pace setter in developing effective environmental policies and setting the pace in aesthetically appealing environments. This will involve reorientation campaigns, aggressive waste reduction and recycling activities, waste disposal with industrial or development involvement, and sewage and organic waste processing. Some of the potential benefits will include:

- Promotion of business and public services including employment generation
- Infrastructure development and industrialisation
- Public health protection and wellbeing of the citizenry
- Environmental health protection and preservation of the natural environment
- Present a platform for sustainable development and community

REFERENCES

Shaker, R.R. (2015). The spatial distribution of development in Europe and its underlying sustainability correlations. Applied Geography, 63, 304-314. doi.org/10.1016/j.apgeog.2015.07.009

Blewitt (2015), p. 7

Lynn R. Kahle, Eda Gurel-Atay, Eds (2014). Communicating Sustainability for the Green Economy. New York: M.E. Sharpe. ISBN 978-0-7656-3680-5.

Finn (2009), pp. 3–8

Ulrich Grober: Deep roots — A conceptual history of "sustainable development" (Nachhaltigkeit), Wissenschaftszentrum Berlin für Sozialforschung, 2007

Blewitt (2015), pp. 6–16

World Conservation Strategy: Living Resource Conservation for Sustainable Development (PDF). International Union for Conservation of Nature and Natural Resources. 1980.

Sachs (2015), p. 4

World Charter for Nature, United Nations, General Assembly, 48th Plenary Meeting, October 28, 1982

Brundtland Commission (1987). "Report of the World Commission on Environment and Development". United Nations.

Smith, Charles; Rees, Gareth (1998). Economic Development, 2nd edition. Basingstoke: Macmillan. ISBN 0-333-72228-0.

Sachs (2015), p. 5

Will Allen. 2007."Learning for Sustainability: Sustainable Development."

Liam Magee; Andy Scerri; Paul James; James A. Thom; Lin Padgham; Sarah Hickmott; Hepu Deng; Felicity Cahill (2013). "Reframing social sustainability reporting: Towards an engaged approach". Environment, Development and Sustainability. University of Melbourne. doi:10.1007/s10668-012-9384-2.

Passet, René (1979-01-01). L'Économique et le vivant (in French). Payot.

United Nations (2014). Prototype Global Sustainable Development Report (Online unedited ed.). New York: United Nations Department of Economic and Social Affairs, Division for Sustainable Development.

James, Paul; with Magee, Liam; Scerri, Andy; Steger, Manfred B. (2015). Urban Sustainability in Theory and Practice: Circles of Sustainability. London: Routledge.

Circles of Sustainability Urban Profile Process and Scerri, Andy; James, Paul (2010). "Accounting for sustainability: Combining qualitative and quantitative research in developing 'indicators' of sustainability". International Journal of Social Research Methodology. 13 (1): 41–53. doi:10.1080/13645570902864145.

http://citiesprogramme.com/aboutus/our-approach/circles-of-sustainability; Scerri, Andy; James, Paul (2010). "Accounting for sustainability: Combining qualitative and quantitative research in developing 'indicators' of sustainability". International Journal of Social Research Methodology. 13 (1): 41–53. doi:10.1080/13645570902864145..

White, F; Stallones, L; Last, JM. (2013). Global Public Health: Ecological Foundations. Oxford University Press. ISBN 978-0-19-975190-7.

Bringing human health and wellbeing back into sustainable development. In: IISD Annual Report 2011-12. http://www.iisd.org/pdf/2012/annrep_2011_2012_en.pdf

IPCC Fifth Assessment Report (2014). "Climate Change 2014: Impacts, Adaptation and Vulnerability" (PDF). Geneva (Switzerland): IPCC.

See Horizon 2020 – the EU's new research and innovation programme http://europa.eu/rapid/press-release_MEMO-13-1085_en.htm

"Flexible strategies for long-term sustainability under uncertainty". Building Research. 40: 545–557. 2012. doi:10.1080/09613218.2012.702565.

Zhang, S.X.; V. Babovic (2012). *"A real options approach to the design and architecture of water supply systems using innovative water technologies under uncertainty" (PDF). Journal of Hydroinformatics.*

Daly, H. E. *Economics, Ecology, Ethics: Essays toward a Steady-State Economy.* Hardin, G. *"The tragedy of the commons". New York and San Francisco: W. H. Freeman and Company. pp. 100–114.*

Networld-Project (1998-02-09). *"Environmental Glossary". Green-networld.com. Retrieved 2011-09-28.*

Ben Falk, *The resilient farm and homestead: An innovative permaculture and whole systems design approach.* Chelsea Green, 2013. pp. 61-78.

Manning, Stephen; Boons, Frank; Von Hagen, Oliver; Reinecke, Juliane (2012). *"National Contexts Matter: The Co-Evolution of Sustainability Standards in Global Value Chains". Ecological Economics.* 83: 197–209. doi:10.1016/j.ecolecon.2011.08.029.

Reinecke, Juliane; Manning, Stephen; Von Hagen, Oliver (2012). *"The Emergence of a Standards Market: Multiplicity of Sustainability Standards in the Global Coffee Industry". Organization Studies.* 33 (5/6): 789–812.

Barbier, Edward B. (2006). *Natural Resources and Economic Development. https://books.google.com/books?id=fYrEDA-VnyUC&pg=PA45: Cambridge University Press.* pp. 44–45. ISBN 9780521706513. Retrieved April 8, 2014.

Korowitz, David (2012), *Ignorance by Consensus, Foundation for the Economics of Sustainability*

Brown, L. R. (2011). *World on the Edge. Earth Policy Institute. Norton. ISBN 978-0-393-08029-2.*

Malte Faber. (2008). How to be an ecological economist. *Ecological Economics* 66(1):1-7. Preprint.

Stivers, R. 1976. The Sustainable Society: Ethics and Economic Growth. Philadelphia: Westminster Press.

Meadows, D.H., D.L. Meadows, J. Randers, and W.W. Behrens III. 1972. The Limits to Growth. Universe Books, New York, NY. ISBN 0-87663-165-0

Meadows, D.H.; Randers, Jørgen; Meadows, D.L. (2004). *Limits to Growth: The 30-Year Update. Chelsea Green Publishing. ISBN 978-1-931498-58-6.*

Daly, Herman E. (1992). *Steady-state economics (2nd ed.). London: Earthscan Publications.*

Barbier, E. (1987). *"The Concept of Sustainable Economic Development". Environmental Conservation.* 14 (2): 101–110. doi:10.1017/S0376892900011449.

Hamilton, K.; Clemens, M. (1999). *"Genuine savings rates in developing countries". World Bank Economy Review.* 13 (2): 333–356. doi:10.1093/wber/13.2.333.

Ayong Le Kama, A. D. (2001). *"Sustainable growth renewable resources, and pollution". Journal of Economic Dynamics and Control.* 25 (12): 1911–1918. doi:10.1016/S0165-1889(00)00007-5.

Stavins, R.; Wagner, A.; Wagner, G. *"Interpreting Sustainability in Economic Terms: Dynamic Efficiency Plus Intergenerational Equity". Economic Letters.* 79 (3): 339–343. doi:10.1016/S0165-1765(03)00036-3.

The History of Development, 3rd Ed. (New York: Zed, 2008) 194.

Daniel P. Castillo, "Integral Ecology as a Liberationist Concept" in *Theological Studies*, Vol 77, 2, June 2016, 374.

Michael Goldman, *Imperial Nature: the World Bank and the Struggle for Justice in the Age of Globalization*. (New Haven: Yale University, 2005), 128, quoted in *Theological Studies*, supra.

Pezzey, John C. V.; Michael A., Toman (2002). "The Economics of Sustainability: A Review of Journal Articles" (PDF). Resources for the future. Retrieved April 8, 2014.

Arrow, K. J.; Dasgupta, P.; Goulder, L.; Daily, G.; Ehrlich, P. R.; Heal, G. M.; Levin, S.; Maler, K-G.; Schneider, S.; Starrett, D. A.; Walker, B. (2004). "Are we consuming too much?". Journal of Economic Perspectives. 18 (3): 147–172. doi:10.1257/0895330042162377. JSTOR 3216811.

Dasgupta, P. (2007). "The idea of sustainable development". Sustainability Science. 2 (1): 5–11. doi:10.1007/s11625-007-0024-y.

Heal, G. (2009). "Climate Economics: A Meta-Review and Some Suggestions for Future Research". Review of Environmental Economics and Policy. 3 (1): 4–21. doi:10.1093/reep/ren014.

Heal, Geoffrey (2009). "Climate Economics: A Meta-Review and Some Suggestions for Future Research". Review of Environmental Economics and Policy. Oxford Journals. 3: 4–21. doi:10.1093/reep/ren014. Retrieved April 8, 2014.

« L'économie politique du développement durable », John Baden, document de l'ICREI Environmental Economics, 3rd Edition. J.J. Seneca/M.K. Taussig. 1984. Page 3.

Fainstein, Susan S. 2000. "New Directions in Planning Theory," *Urban Affairs Review* 35:4 (March)

Bedsworf, Louise W. and Ellen Hanak. 2010. "Adaptation to Climate Change, "Journal of the American Planning Association, 76:4.

http://www.ren21.net/wp-content/uploads/2015/07/REN12-GSR2015_Onlinebook_low1.pdf pg31

Campbell, Scott. 1996. "Green Cities, Growing Cities, Just Cities?: Urban planning and the Contradictions of Sustainable Development," Journal of the American Planning Association

Farah, Paolo Davide (2015). "Sustainable Energy Investments and National Security: Arbitration and Negotiation Issues". JOURNAL OF WORLD ENERGY LAW AND BUSINESS. 8 (6). Retrieved 26 November 2015.

Hazeltine, B.; Bull, C. (1999). Appropriate Technology: Tools, Choices, and Implications. New York: Academic Press. pp. 3, 270. ISBN 0-12-335190-1.

Akubue, Anthony (Winter–Spring 2000). "Appropriate Technology for Socioeconomic Development in Third World Countries". The Journal of Technology Studies. 26 (1): 33–43. Retrieved March 2011. Check date values in: |access-date= (help)

Pearce, Joshua M. (2012). "The Case for Open Source Appropriate Technology". Environment, Development and Sustainability. 14 (3): 425–431. doi:10.1007/s10668-012-9337-9.

Pearce J., Albritton S., Grant G., Steed G., & Zelenika I. 2012. A new model for enabling innovation in appropriate technology for sustainable development. *Sustainability: Science, Practice, & Policy* 8(2), pp. 42-53, 2012.

I. Zelenika and J.M. Pearce, Innovation Through Collaboration: Scaling up Technological Solutions for Sustainable Development, *Environment, Development and Sustainability* 16(6): 1299-1316 (2014). doi:10.1007/s10668-014-9528-7

Buehler, Ralph; Pucher, John (2011). "Sustainable Transport in Freiburg: Lessons from Germany's Environmental Capital". International Journal of Sustainable Transportation. 5: 43–70. doi:10.1080/15568311003650531.

"LEDS in Practice: Breathe clean". The Low Emission Development Strategies Global Partnership.

"LEDS in Practice: Create jobs". The Low Emission Development Strategies Global Partnership.

"LEDS in Practice: Make roads safe". The Low Emission Development Strategies Global Partnership.

"LEDS in Practice: Save money and time". The Low Emission Development Strategies Global Partnership.

Barbour, Elissa and Elizabeth A. Deakin. 2012. "Smart Growth Planning for Climate Protection"

Murthy, A.S. Narasimha Mohle, Henry. Transportation Engineering Basics (2nd Edition). (American Society of Cilil Engineers 2001).

Printed in Great Britain
by Amazon

83423406R00047